the sacraments in a world of change

the sacraments in a world of change

joseph m. champlin

AVE MARIA PRESS / NOTRE DAME / INDIANA 46556

Acknowledgments:

NC News Service for selected columns published originally in the *Know Your Faith* series, © 1970, 1971, 1972

Confraternity of Christian Doctrine, Washington, D.C., for excerpts from the *New American Bible* © 1970. All rights reserved

CRUX Information Service for an excerpt from the document on *Pastoral Norms Concerning the Administration of General Sacramental Absolution*

Excerpts from the English translations of the *Rite of Baptism for Children, Revised Order of Confirmation (provisional text), General Instruction of the Roman Missal, Rite of Marriage, Rite of Funerals* and *Rites for the Sick* (provisional text). Copyright © 1969, 1970, 1971, International Committee on English in the Liturgy, Inc. All rights reserved

Orbis Books, Maryknoll, New York—for an excerpt from *Christ Present and Yet to Come* © 1971

United States Catholic Conference—for excerpts from the *General Catechetical Directory* © 1971; the NCWC translation of the encyclical *Mystici Corporis* and the *Constitution on the Sacred Liturgy*. All rights reserved. Used with permission

Nihil Obstat: John L. Reedy, C.S.C.
Censor Deputatus

Imprimatur: Most Rev. Leo A. Pursley, D.D.
Bishop of Fort Wayne/South Bend

Library of Congress Catalog Card Number: 73-83347

International Standard Book Number: 0-87793-085-6

Cover photo: NASA

Printed in the United States of America

To my sister, Nancy, her husband, David,
and their four children.

contents

introduction

This volume, like its companion, *The Mass in a World of Change,* grew out of a series of columns written over a two-year span and published under the title "Worship and the World" as part of the NC News Service *Know Your Faith* adult education program which has appeared weekly in some 90 Catholic diocesan papers.

It is a selection of the more pertinent material carefully edited. In addition, readers will find at the conclusion of each chapter a few relevant quotations from official documents and several discussion questions linked with the content of that unit.

Those of you who have read my previous volume, *Christ Present and Yet to Come,* will recognize in the final chapters of this text occasional excerpts or illustrations from that publication.

The seven chapters of this book do not treat all the sacraments (Holy Orders is omitted), but they do cover the most significant moments and events of a person's life — birth, growth, maturity, guilt, love, sickness and death. There are, of course, sacred rites and liturgies as well as unique sacraments in the Roman Catholic Church designed for each of these circumstances. The pages which follow offer neither an in-depth nor an exhaustive study of the sacraments according to those recently revised rituals. Instead, they sketch salient features of the renewed texts, describe some actual situations in which these rites have been employed with success, and suggest possible directions for them in the future.

It is my hope that this book and its companion will prove helpful for parish and diocesan liturgy commissions, for adult study groups, for high school or college classes, as well as for individuals interested in the liturgical renewal.

I would like here to thank the NC News Staff for their assistance in preparing my weekly column and the editors at Ave Maria Press for their aid in readying those articles for publication as a book. Moreover, I offer a word of gratitude to Miss Florence Froio who typed and collated the manuscript.

part 1 / beginning a new life

The Rite of Baptism for Children

"Christian Initiation," General Introduction

1. Through the sacraments of Christian initiation men and women are freed from the power of darkness. With Christ they die, are buried and rise again. They receive the Spirit of adoption which makes them God's sons and daughters and, with the entire people of God, they celebrate the memorial of the Lord's death and resurrection.

2. Through baptism men and women are incorporated into Christ. They are formed into God's people, and they obtain forgiveness of all their sins. They are raised from their natural human condition to the dignity of adopted children. They become a new creation through water and the Holy Spirit. Hence they are called, and are indeed, the children of God.

Signed with the gift of the Spirit in confirmation, Christians more perfectly become the image of their Lord and are filled with the Holy Spirit. They bear witness to him before all the world and eagerly work for the building up of the body of Christ.

Finally they come to the table of the eucharist, to eat the flesh and drink the blood of the Son of Man so that they may have eternal life and show forth the unity of God's people. By offering themselves with Christ, they share in his universal sacrifice: the entire community of the redeemed is offered to God by their high priest. They pray for a greater outpouring of the Holy Spirit so that the whole human race may be brought into the unity of God's family.

Thus the three sacraments of Christian initiation closely combine to bring the faithful to the full stature of Christ and to enable them to carry out the mission of the entire people of God in the Church and in the world.

Parents and the New Baptismal Rite

You no doubt remember and celebrate each year the anniversary of your "birth in the flesh." But do you know the date of your "birth in the Spirit"? And do you yearly on the day of your Baptism, renew a promise to die with Christ and thus rise with him, or remake this commitment to accept Jesus and reject Satan?

Those who designed the new baptismal rite for infants hope its features will so facilitate involvement of parents in this ceremony that as a consequence their children ultimately will in fact yearly recall and respond to the implications of Baptism.

We have during past decades too often regarded infant Baptism as something of a "magic" event. Priest, water and words were the essential elements. Perhaps two, probably one, possibly none of the parents participated in the service. Godparents stood by implicitly promising to supply a Christian education for the child in the event mother and dad failed to fulfill their responsibilities. Grace flowed, as it were, almost automatically.

The reformed rite takes a different approach. Introductory guidelines to the ritual state its emphasis clearly and simply: "Because of natural relationships, parents have a more important ministry and role in the baptism of infants than the godparents . . . . It is very important that the parents should be present in the celebration in which their child is reborn in water and the Holy Spirit . . . . They (and especially the mother) carry the child to the font."

The latter point represents a radical departure from our tradition in the United States. Generally, mothers have either remained at home or kept in the background until "churched" afterwards. Now we expect the mother to hold the baby and the father to accompany his wife. Why? Because we believe that infants "are baptized in the faith of the Church," a faith "proclaimed for them by their parents and godparents."

To proclaim this faith for a tiny baby, to ask for the child's Baptism presupposes a willingness to form, educate and train that adopted son of God in the good news of Christ. Unless parents are ready to assume the responsibility for such an education, it would seem the infant should not be baptized. At least this is how I interpret the following words directed in our new service to father and mother after they request Baptism for their child:

"You have asked to have your child baptized. In doing so you are accepting the responsibility of training him (her) in the practice of the faith. It will be your duty to bring him (her) up to keep God's commandments as Christ taught us, by loving God and our neighbor. Do you clearly understand what you are undertaking?" Parents respond with: "We do."

A similar, but shorter, charge is given to the godparents: "Are you ready to help these parents in their duty as Christian mothers and fathers?" They say: "We are."

Msgr. Joseph Moriarty, a longtime lover of the liturgy from Cleveland, Ohio, suggests a practical measure which might aid parents in this ongoing task of Christian formation for the child. The reformed ritual reads: "Someone from each family (e.g., the father or godfather) lights the child's candle from the Easter candle." That burning flame symbolizes the light of faith in this baby's heart; the Risen Lord now dwells in a unique way within the baptized child. Hopefully the light will never be extinguished or the guest driven out.

The Cleveland priest suggests that lighting this candle at the anniversary baptismal day and placing it on the supper table could be a silent sign for the first years. Later, with a gradually maturing grasp of the flame's significance, the young Christian would year after year reaffirm in words vows repeated for him (or her) at Baptism.

Children from families with such a home practice (which will be described in detail later on) certainly will never forget the day of their birth in the Spirit. The odds are also much better that people from backgrounds like this will, as independent adults, respond with free, personal faith to the Lord and his message. They will, it seems to me, be more disposed to accept on their own the dignity and duty of Christians which concerned parents asked and assumed for them at the moment of Baptism.

Fresh, Flowing Water

St. Richard's Church in Jackson, Mississippi, won an architectural award a few years back. Its massive, poured-concrete structure and plain interior walls seem too stark or cold for some. But many feel that the building, designed carefully for the revised liturgy by its well-known pastor, Msgr. Josiah Chatham, and artist Frank Kacmarcik, is a perfect setting for public worship.

To reach the church proper, visitors walk through a relatively long, narrow, and high-walled passageway (labeled the "moat" by several local clergy). Once inside the door, you encounter a huge — about five feet in diameter—baptismal font filled with fresh and flowing water.

The nature and location of this baptistry says something. It speaks, first, of the truth that Baptism brings us into the Church, makes us Christians, ushers us into a community of those who believe in Jesus. As we dip our hand in the water and make the sign of the cross, we should be reminded of another fundamental fact about our faith. God chose a quite ordinary, very necessary, and frequently employed element to save men. "Unless a man is reborn in water and the Holy Spirit, he cannot enter the kingdom of God" (Jn 3:5).

The baptismal candle lighted on the anniversary

date and placed at the supper table could, as previously suggested, help us yearly to remember and renew vows made in Baptism. Holy water, the sign of the cross, and the strategically situated baptismal font might accomplish that same purpose on a weekly, even daily basis.

God has used water consistently in the course of history to heal and make holy, to correct and cleanse. Noah's ark and the flood, the Exodus from Egypt with its walls of Red Sea water stand as classic examples. But we also must cite the ceremonial washings prescribed in Old Testament times, the repentant bath preached by John the Baptist, the miracles Jesus wrought through water ("Go, wash." "I went, I washed, and I see" Jn 9).

In reforming the baptismal ritual, Church authorities hoped to accentuate those points of our religious heritage. Thus true water, for the sake of "authentic sacramental symbolism," is required and it should be clean, "for reasons of health." The following directive highlights a particularly significant change in this service:

"Outside the Easter season, it is desirable that the water be blessed for each occasion, in order that the words of blessing may clearly express the mystery of salvation which the Church recalls and proclaims. If the baptistry is supplied with flowing water, the blessing will be given to the water as it flows."

Msgr. Chatham was indeed a man ahead of his times. At St. Richard's, the special baptismal water (mixed with sacred oils and blessed at Easter time) had been kept in a compartment near the font. It alone was poured on the head of each infant in accord with regulations of the older rite. However, according to the reformed ritual, the celebrant now need only bless fresh water at every Baptism with words and a touch of his hand. "Lord, make holy this water which you have created, so that all those you have chosen may be born again by the power of the

Holy Spirit, and may take their place among your holy people." The other portions of this blessing and the added, optional texts further specify the meaning of this gesture by explicitly mentioning several instances of sacred history in which God has intervened with water as his effective instrument.

Baptismal fonts like the one in Jackson are obviously well suited for this new rite. In addition, they seem ideal for Baptism by immersion, a practice deemed more desirable, in the words of the official texts, "as a symbol of participation in the death and resurrection of Christ." Nevertheless, the more customary ceremony by infusion is still permitted and at least in the immediate future probably will be the more standard procedure.

Our understanding of Baptism continues to develop. Scholars and parish priests today emphasize this sacrament's relationship to the Eucharist. For that and for several other reasons many experts now would opt for a baptismal font in the front of a church rather than at its entrance. Msgr. Chatham agrees and admits that, were he to build again, his baptistry would be located in the sanctuary, near the altar, but opposite the pulpit. We will treat that question next.

Baptism at Sunday Mass

Father Donald Krebs graduated from Notre Dame in the early 50's, studied at the seminary in St. Paul, and serves now as a priest of the Crookston, Minnesota, diocese. While pastor of St. Joseph's Church in Middle River, he shepherded a tiny flock and led them at worship in the handsome church with its excellent pipe organ. An active member of the diocesan liturgy and music commission, Father Krebs, like many of today's priests, feels a need for constant, personal updating in theology. This pushes him to spend several weeks during the summer at St. John's in Collegeville studying Sacred Scripture, liturgy and other related subjects.

These refresher courses help. When this pastor returns to his parish, he finds himself more aware of current developments and in a better position to introduce the latest liturgical reforms — like baptizing within Mass.

The revised rite for infant Baptism suggests: "On Sunday, baptism may be celebrated even during Mass, so that the entire community may be present and the necessary relationship between baptism and eucharist may be clearly seen, but this should not be done too often" (no. 9).

This simply carries to a logical conclusion the notion that Baptism is basically a service of initiation, a welcoming of child (or adult) into the Christian community, into the Church. The introduction to *Christian Initiation* reiterates the thought with these words: "In the actual celebration, the people of God (represented not only by the parents, godparents and relatives, but also, as far as possible, by friends, neighbors, and some members of the local church) should take an active part. Thus they will show their common faith and express their joy as the newly baptized are received into the community of the Church" (art. 7).

There are not a great number of Baptisms at St. Joseph's, perhaps a dozen each year. This makes it possible to baptize every infant (with the exception of cases where parents, especially the mother, might be embarrassed) within the context of a Sunday Eucharist. The reaction to this innovation, begun soon after the implementation date for the new ritual, seems very positive. Parents naturally enjoy "showing off" the gift of life they have received and their signing of this child at the rite of welcome in particular impresses those in the congregation. Parishioners likewise appear favorable to the new procedure. They sing up something of a storm for the occasion and their response to various prayers makes it clear this celebration is a community event.

The reformed ritual reminds us that "the faith in which the children are baptized is not the private possession of the individual family, but is the common treasure of the whole Church of Christ" (no. 4). We see this truth acted out, as it were, immediately before the Baptism proper when celebrant and congregation assent to the profession of faith. The priest says: "This is our faith. This is the faith of the Church. We are proud to profess it, in Christ Jesus our Lord." All lend their support to his words with an "Amen." Father Krebs finds his parishioners understand well the significance of this part of the ceremony and truly do express their faith with a strong united "Amen."

In our contemporary concern about time, one might worry over the added moments required to include Baptism at Mass. The fear is unfounded. At St. Joseph's a eucharistic liturgy which incorporates within it this rite of Christian initiation lasts but five minutes longer than the regular Sunday service. The celebrant there observes directives in the official text which outline that combined rite.

According to these guidelines, the reception of children replaces the greeting and penitential rite; a liturgy of the word with reading, homily, general intercessions, but no Creed follows the opening prayer; the celebration of Baptism itself begins at the prayer of exorcism and continues through to, but excluding the concluding rite; the celebrant resumes Mass at the preparation of gifts and, for the final blessing, may use one of the solemn baptismal benedictions.

The Minnesota pastor, after several experiences with Baptism at Mass, stopped providing companion booklets for the congregation. He found that these pamphlets, far from facilitating the people's understanding of the ceremony, actually interfered with parishioners' participation in the celebration. Their noses were buried in the books, their eyes fixed on the printed page instead of upon the living event before them. He found that a brief explanation, a few words of prompting elicited much better responses. Father Krebs believes that the service itself does the explaining; the ritual, in his view, should be so designed that it is self-explanatory.

That thinking rests on a solid foundation. The Council Fathers decreed that the reformed liturgical rites should be "short, clear, and unencumbered by useless repetitions; they should be within the people's powers of comprehension, and normally should not require much explanation" (art. 34).

Baptism and the Home

In swimming pools or at the beach these days, one sees fewer men with Catholic religious medals hanging about their necks. Our churches have taken on a simpler style, almost stark and barren for some, with only one or two statues, few paintings or mosaics, and only the plain beauty of straight colors or unpainted surfaces to decorate an interior. We make the sign of the cross less often in public. Holy water fonts for home or school have practically disappeared.

I am not arguing here for or against this trend to discard traditional signs and ritualistic gestures associated with Catholicism. I only note these quite obvious facts. It is interesting, however, to observe that in the "secular" world around us, especially among the young, symbols and "sacred rites" abound. The Woodstock festival had them, Volkswagens bear them on their bodies, contemporary movies are filled with them.

One Roman Catholic sign or symbol *not* in decline is the baptismal candle presented to parents at a child's initiation into the Church. Officials for firms producing these items tell me sales have increased over recent months and parish priests frequently comment on how pleased people are with this personal candle given to them during the ceremony. The clergy, of course, hope the gift not only will teach the child and parents about the sacrament's meaning but also may help father and mother in the Christian formation of a son or daughter. The revised rite explicitly mentions this and places a serious educational responsibility upon those who bring infants to the saving waters for Baptism.

"To fulfill the true meaning of the sacrament, children must later be formed in the faith in which they have been baptized. The foundation of this formation will be the sacrament itself, which they have already received. Christian formation, which is their due, seeks to lead them gradually to learn God's plan in Christ, so that they may ultimately accept for themselves the faith in which they have been baptized" (no. 3).

"After baptism it is the responsibility of the parents, in their gratitude to God and in fidelity to the duty they have undertaken, to enable the child to know God, whose adopted child it has become, to receive confirmation, and to participate in the holy eucharist. In this duty they are to be helped by the parish priest by suitable means" (no. 5, section 5).

The Will and Baumer Candle Company (Syracuse, New York 13201) has printed a leaflet, "The Light of Christ," to accompany their baptismal candle. It could prove helpful to parents in the later and gradual Christian education of children. The six-page publication outlines parental responsibility, sketches the meaning of initiation, the paschal mystery and the baptismal candle, and suggests an anniversary service for the renewal of those vows made in a baby's name by the parents. Like other similar businesses, Will and Baumer manufactures a special candle for Baptism and a companion box with space for the names of those involved in the ceremony and the date of the sacrament's administration. A "Light of Christ" leaflet naturally goes along with each set, but I know the company would be happy to mail free single copies on request and will supply quantity amounts at the cost of printing to priests or others who might find them useful.

The baptismal anniversary service takes place in a home, presumably at the main meal and with the special candle lighted either for the entire dinner or only during the actual ceremony. An annual invitation to godparents, when possible, obviously would heighten the occasion. It could be a way to tell godparents silently, but rather powerfully, how important they are in the eyes of the family and the child.

A reading of one, two or more pertinent selections from the bible starts the rite, sets the mood, speaks to those present about the sacrament and highlights God's presence at the ceremony through his Word. This leaflet lists the 21 Old and New Testament passages included in our official ritual for Baptism. After some comments and a period of silent reflection, the father or someone from the family (termed reader) begins the repetition of vows with these following or some comparable words. (I will name the baptized person Mary for sake of simplicity.)

"Some time ago we presented Mary for Baptism. By water and the Holy Spirit she received the gift of new life from God, who is love. On our part we have made it our constant care to bring Mary up in the practice of the faith. We have tried to see that the divine life which God gave be kept from the poison of sin and might grow always stronger in Mary's heart. We share a common faith, the faith of the Church, and it was in this faith Mary was baptized. At that time we rejected sin and professed our faith in Christ Jesus. Now that you, Mary, are older and your faith makes you ready to accept this responsibility, we ask you to renew the vows of your own baptism."

If the child is not old enough to profess these promises, the parents and godparents do so in his or her name. The renewal formula involves that same rejection of evil and acceptance of Jesus which took place some time earlier at a church baptistry before the sacramental washing with water.

Next, the leader says: "Mary you have renewed the vows of your baptism. You are called a child of God, for so you are. In confirmation you will receive the fullness of God's spirit. In holy communion you will share the banquet of Christ's sacrifice calling God your Father in the midst of the Church. In your name, all of us, sharing a common sonship, now pray together in the words our Lord gave us. . . ."

The Lord's Prayer and a multiple blessing by the leader with an "Amen" by all present concludes this service.

Such a simple ceremony will not necessarily solve for parents every difficulty in the religious training of a child nor assure the infant's acceptance of Christ at adulthood. But it should facilitate efforts and certainly will fix the date of Baptism firmly in everyone's mind.

Baptize When Parents Don't Care?

I think it was the Legion of Mary handbook which made this observation: Some persons will dash full-speed into heaven, others will creep there, and a few must be pushed through those gates leading to eternal life.

That illustration describes rather well the various degrees of religious commitment or concern we find in Christian parents. Some take the responsibilities they assume relative to the spiritual training of their children very seriously; others fulfill the minimum requirements, but without enthusiasm; a few neglect even the basic duties.

However, most "nonpracticing" Catholic parents, mothers especially, do worry a bit about the Baptism of their offspring. True, they may not quite get to it for several months or a few years. But generally, despite the flesh's weakness, the spirit seems more than willing.

What should be done when people who seldom worship on Sunday suddenly bring a tiny, or maybe not so tiny, baby to church for Baptism? What about those parents who have not confessed or communicated in a decade? What policy must we follow—and this is the more difficult question—if mother and dad give little religious instruction in the home and make only feeble efforts to see that some is received outside the house?

The new baptismal rite exacts a promise from parents to train the child "in the practice of the faith." From that we could argue for a hard-line attitude toward such religiously marginal people: Prove you are good Catholics—a conscientious Christian mother and father—or forget about the Baptism.

On the other hand, neither life (frequently complex) nor Christ (the wheat and the weeds) nor the Church (sacraments are for the people) operates in that fashion. The revised ritual demonstrates something of this flexibility when it states:

"If one of the parents cannot make the profession of faith. . . , he may keep silent." The Church only asks that when Baptism is requested for the child, arrangements should be made or permission given "for the child to be instructed in the faith of its baptism."

We understandably stress on the occasion of a Baptism the duties of parents and hope they will follow through afterwards. After all, no one can transmit the heritage of our Christian faith as well as a believing, praying, loving mother or father. But, to keep matters in perspective, "the faith in which the children are baptized is not the private possession of the individual family, but is the common treasure of the whole church of Christ."

Jesus was patient with sinners, understood the weak, preferred to fan a flickering flame rather than to snuff it out. The Church cannot do otherwise. It seeks to preserve and spread this faith, this common treasure under both the best and the poorest of circumstances, through the parents or in spite of them.

Our Canadian neighbors in the Montreal archdiocese have tried to resolve in practice those earlier questions I posed. Their Pastoral Liturgical Service in an August 13, 1971, document, *The Baptism of Children Born of Non-Practicing Parents,* includes this sensible and sensitive paragraph:

"Baptism should not be refused to a child on the

grounds that the parents no longer 'practice' although they still affirm their belief in God and in the Church. The fact that some parents ask that their child receive baptism proves, to some extent at least, that they have a minimum of faith in God and that they hold to retaining a link with the Church even though that faith is not apparent exteriorly and the link with the Church seems weak. Why should we 'quench the smoking flax' and risk breaking that bond with the Church? On the contrary, this would provide an excellent occasion for each pastor to revive this wavering faith and to strengthen this link."

. . .

From the Rite of Baptism for Children

(General Introduction to Christian Initiation, continued)

I. Dignity of Baptism

3. Baptism is the door to life and to the kingdom of God. Christ offered this first sacrament of the new law to all men that they might have eternal life. He entrusted this sacrament and the gospel to his Church when he told his apostles: "Go, make disciples of all nations, and baptize them in the name of the Father, and of the Son, and of the Holy Spirit." Therefore baptism is, above all, the sacrament of that faith by which men and women, enlightened by the Spirit's grace, respond to the gospel of Christ. That is why the Church believes it is her most basic and necessary duty to inspire all, catechumens, parents of children still to be baptized, and godparents, to that true and living faith by which they adhere to Christ and enter into or confirm their commitment to the new covenant. To accomplish this, the Church prescribes the pastoral instruction of catechumens, the preparation of the children's parents, the celebration of God's word, and the profession of baptismal faith.

4. Further, baptism is the sacrament by which men and women are incorporated into the Church, built into a house where God lives, in the Spirit, into a holy nation and a royal priesthood. It is a sacramental bond of unity linking all who have been signed by it. Because of that unchangeable effect (signified in the Latin liturgy by the anointing of the baptized person with chrism in the presence of God's people), the rite of baptism is held in highest honor by all Christians. It may never lawfully be repeated once it has been validly celebrated, even if by fellow Christians from whom we are separated.

5. Baptism, the cleansing with water by the power of the living Word, makes us sharers in God's own life and his adopted children. As proclaimed in the prayers for the blessing of the water, baptism is a cleansing water of rebirth, which makes us God's children. The blessed Trinity is invoked over those who are to be baptized. Signed in this name, they are consecrated to the Trinity and enter into fellowship with the Father, the Son, and the Holy Spirit. They are prepared for this high dignity and led to it by the scriptural readings, the prayer of the community, and the threefold profession of faith.

6. Far superior to the purifications of the old law, baptism produces all these effects by the power of the mystery of the Lord's passion and resurrection. Those who are baptized are engrafted in the likeness of Christ's death. They are buried with him, they are given life again with him, and with him they rise again. For baptism recalls and effects the paschal mystery itself, because by means of it men and women pass from the death of sin into life. Its celebration, there-

fore, should reflect the joy of the resurrection, especially when it takes place during the Easter Vigil or on a Sunday.

II. Offices and Ministries of Baptism

7. Christian instruction and the preparation for baptism are a vital concern of God's people, the Church, which hands on and nourishes the faith it has received from the apostles. Through the ministry of the Church, adults are called by the Holy Spirit to the gospel, and infants are baptized and brought up in this faith. Therefore it is most important that catechists and other lay people should work with priests and deacons in making preparations for baptism. In the actual celebration, the people of God (represented not only by the parents, godparents and relatives, but also, as far as possible, by friends, neighbors, and some members of the local church) should take an active part. Thus they will show their common faith and express their joy as the newly baptized are received into the community of the Church.

2. From the earliest times, the Church, to which the mission of preaching the gospel and of baptizing was entrusted, has baptized children as well as adults. Our Lord said: "Unless a man is reborn in water and the Holy Spirit, he cannot enter the kingdom of God." The Church has always understood these words to mean that children should not be deprived of baptism, because they are baptized in the faith of the Church. This faith is proclaimed for them by their parents and godparents, who represent both the local Church and the whole society of saints and believers: "The Church is at once the mother of all and the mother of each."

3. To fulfill the true meaning of the sacrament, children must later be formed in the faith in which they have been baptized. The foundation of this formation will be the sacrament itself, which they have already received. Christian formation, which is their due, seeks to lead them gradually to learn God's plan in Christ, so that they may ultimately accept for themselves the faith in which they have been baptized.

. . .

DISCUSSION QUESTIONS

1. "In our marriage we are going to let the children make up their own minds about religion." What do you think of that attitude? Of infant Baptism in general?
2. Discuss the meaning of these elements used in the baptismal ceremony: water, oil, the paschal candle, the baptismal candle, the baptismal garment, bible, exorcism.
3. The ritual states: "Except in case of danger of death, Baptism should not be celebrated in private houses." Why not?
4. "I was baptized, but I never joined." Jennie in the movie *Love Story* made this comment about her own religious situation. Does this say anything about the process of Christian initiation?
5. How often should Baptisms be celebrated at the same Sunday Mass?

part 2 / growing up in god's family

Confirmation: How Celebrate It?

Bishop Charles Buswell, a tall, friendly, gentle man who shepherds the small diocese of Pueblo, Colorado, is, in my book, a very, very fine Christian, priest, and bishop. Over the past decade I have watched this servant of the Lord move among people during conventions, and I have read a letter he wrote to one troubled cleric who had resigned from the ministry. I also have noted his courageous, unpopular stands on several delicate issues and heard glowing, firsthand reports about him from Pueblo priests, religious and laity.

The ever-smiling leader shared some of his pastoral insights with diocesan liturgical commission members at a national meeting in San Francisco in October, 1971. He spoke as part of a panel on "Confirmation: How Celebrate It in Our Time?" and suggested several practical ways to improve the liturgy of this sacrament.

Many of those ideas, interestingly enough, are now incorporated into the revised rite of Confirmation issued by the Holy See. In the subsequent sections I will discuss at some length that renewed ritual. Now, however, I would like to recall several of the specific recommendations Bishop Buswell offered us at the convention in California.

He encourages more personal, less assembly-line-like liturgical celebrations for Confirmation. That naturally is easier in smaller areas such as Pueblo than in the huge churches of New York City, but where there is a will we generally can find a way to achieve what we want.

In Bishop Buswell's diocese they try to develop a warm community spirit before the ceremony through a potluck supper at the parish in which bishop, priests, parents, sponsors and children mix and meet. This gives the confirming prelate an opportunity to talk informally with the boys and girls (or adults) and develop a rapport which will carry over to the liturgy which follows soon after the meal.

I think in most instances today the bishop is only a name, an oily hand on the forehead, a distant face which appears on the scene for an hour and then fades away until the next time, an authoritative voice, a man dressed in different clothes. A preparatory meal or some similar gathering in advance could help correct those impressions and create a more human image of the bishop.

Here is an additional step to personalize the ceremony. Normally the bishop moves along from person to person confirming while a choir sings, with or without the congregation, suitable songs to fill up the long, empty interval that results. Bishop Buswell recommends, instead, announcing each individual's name plus the child's parents' and godparents' as Confirmation is conferred.

Since Confirmation forms part of the Christian initiation process and complements Baptism, Pueblo's bishop would like to see the baptismal name retained and employed in the Confirmation liturgy.

For the same reason, and to link Confirmation with the Eucharist, he generally celebrates the sacrament within Mass and communicates all present for the ceremony under both kinds. The Introduction to this restored rite supports him in that practice: "Ordinarily confirmation takes place within Mass in order to express more clearly the fundamental connection of this sacrament with the entirety of Christian initiation. The latter reaches its culmination in the communion of the body and blood of Christ. Therefore, the newly confirmed should participate in the eucharist which completes their Christian initiation."

A final, but significant recommendation: Make full use of the sacramental signs found in the ceremony. For example, sprinkle all present, not just the Confirmation candidates, with holy water after the renewal of baptismal vows. And do so in sufficient quantity to impress on the community that this really is water, that it bears a connection with Baptism, that we reaffirm promises made at the font whenever we cross ourselves with blessed water.

Bishop Buswell likewise strongly urges using generous quantities of oil at the Confirmation rite—and leaving it on afterwards. I always wondered about the wisdom of instant and efficient priest "wipers" who walked after the bishop and immediately rubbed off on carefully prepared pieces of cotton the little chrism cross traced on each candidate's forehead. Sacramental rites are signs which should be visible to our external senses. If we can see the oil and feel it and retain this anointing for a few hours, then perhaps we will understand more clearly the indelible character, the permanent seal of the Lord we have received as a gift from God.

New Rite of Confirmation

On the feast of the Assumption, 1971, Pope Paul VI issued a revised rite for Confirmation. Like the other renewed rituals recently published (e.g., Baptism, marriage, funerals), it contains a variety of alternative texts—readings, prayers, blessings—and expects the bishop in consultation with those who plan the liturgy to select those which best fit the circumstances of a specific congregation.

The new decree, however, also includes several significant changes in the manner in which this sacrament has customarily been administered. I would like briefly to describe a few of those innovations.

—Sponsors. Formerly, Confirmation godparents were to be distinct from the adults who fulfilled that role at Baptism. Nor were parents allowed to "stand up" for their boys or girls during this ceremony. The revised legislation takes a totally different view, even expressly abrogating previous Church law in the process.

"Ordinarily there should be a sponsor for each of those to be confirmed." "It is desirable that the godparent at baptism, if present, also be the sponsor at confirmation." "Even the parents themselves may present their children for confirmation."

Authorities naturally did not introduce those reforms without good reason. Each of the three modifications noted above enjoys sound theological support. The Vatican document explains their doctrinal basis in these terms:

A sponsor for each: "The sponsor brings the candidate to receive the sacrament, presents him to the minister for anointing, and will later help him to fulfill his baptismal promises faithfully under the influence of the Holy Spirit."

The same sponsor for Baptism and Confirmation: "This change expresses more clearly the relationship between baptism and confirmation and also makes the duty and function of the sponsor more effective."

Parents as sponsors: "The initiation of the children into the sacramental life is especially the responsibility and concern of Christian parents. They are to form and gradually increase a spirit of faith in the children and, with the help of catechetical institutions, prepare them for the fruitful reception of the sacraments of confirmation and the Eucharist. The role of the parents is also expressed by their active participation in the celebration of the sacraments."

—Parental preparation of the candidates: "Vatican II statements on Christian education clearly specify that parents are the prime religious teachers of children. This truth has enormous consequences on the practical level, effects already observable in the current country-wide programs of parent involvement in catechesis for first Communion and first confession."

The quotation just cited would seem to encourage a similar approach for Confirmation. However, for the priest simply to throw this educational ball to mother and dad, then walk away, is not exactly what the Roman text recommends. An earlier paragraph notes: "It is the responsibility of the people of God to prepare the baptized for the reception of the sacrament of confirmation. Pastors should see that all the baptized come to the fullness of Christian initiation and are therefore carefully prepared for confirmation."

Parents, as I see the picture, ought to do more, to be more intimately involved in the Confirmation preparation, but in cooperation with others (parish priest, religious instructor, fellow parishioners), not to the exclusion of them.

—Priest assistants for the bishop. The latter was the original minister of Confirmation and as a consequence "ordinarily the sacrament is administered by the bishop so that there will be a more evident relationship to the first pouring of the Holy Spirit on the day of Pentecost. After they were filled with the Holy Spirit, the apostles themselves gave the Spirit to the faithful through the laying on of their hands. In this way, the reception of the Spirit through the ministry of the bishop shows the close bond which joins the confirmed to the Church and the mandate of Christ to be witnesses among men."

Nevertheless, the law now gives certain others the authority to confirm in special situations. Of particular interest, in my mind, is this provision: "In case of true necessity and special reason, for example, the large number of persons to be confirmed, the minister of confirmation may associate other priests with himself in the administration of this sacrament."

Among those listed are "the pastors of the places where confirmation is conferred, pastors of the places where the candidates belong, or priests who have taken a special part in the catechetical preparation of the candidates."

This solves a particular problem for us in the United States. It makes Confirmation within Mass not only a desirable goal, but a practical possibility. But more on that next.

Confirmation: Within or Without Mass

Do you remember your own Confirmation, or the last time you attended that ceremony? Was it within the context of a Mass, or did it perhaps conclude with benediction of the Blessed Sacrament?

I have no facts from any survey indicating what is standard practice throughout the United States. My own diocese, however, in the face of seemingly endless difficulties arising from the great number of parishes and candidates, has as long as I can remember avoided the celebration of Confirmation at Mass. I would guess that might be true as well in most other areas.

The revised rite for this sacrament calls for a change and recommends the administration of Confirmation within a eucharistic service.

One rubric (no. 51) simply observes that "it is most proper that confirmation be conferred during Mass."

An earlier directive (no. 13), as we have seen, reiterates this guidance and, more importantly, gives an explanation for it. "Ordinarily confirmation takes place within Mass in order to express more clearly the fundamental connection of this sacrament with the entirety of Christian initiation. The latter reaches its culmination in the communion of the body and blood of Christ. Therefore, the newly confirmed should participate in the Eucharist which completes their Christian initiation."

True enough, the renewed ritual provides for a service outside of a eucharistic celebration. Nevertheless, that ceremony is for special circumstances only; under normal conditions and as a basic ideal the Roman document urges Confirmation at Mass.

The ritual outlines quite specifically, in a manner similar to the baptismal text, how the sacrament should be administered within the Eucharist.

1. After the scriptural readings (special for Confirmation), the bishop delivers an instruction or homily (the text offers a sample one). This might well be "in a kind of dialogue, especially with children."

2. Candidates renew baptismal promises following the bishop's words (the ordinary profession of faith is therefore omitted).

3. Next comes the imposition of hands, anointing and general intercessions.

4. Rubrics encourage some of the confirmed persons afterwards to bring forward gifts for the liturgy of the Eucharist.

5. Confirmed adults, their sponsors, parents, spouses and instructors may receive Communion under both kinds.

6. A special blessing in place of the customary concluding benediction is provided in the restored rite.

All of this must sound beautiful, but hopelessly idealistic to the diocesan master of ceremonies or bishop's secretary who must schedule several Confirmations on the same day and for candidates in the hundreds. The new regulations, however, come to his rescue in two ways.

First of all, while hoping that "the minister of confirmation celebrate the Mass, or better concelebrate the Mass," it allows an alternative. "If the Mass is celebrated by someone else, it is proper that the bishop preside over the liturgy of the word and that he give the blessing at the end of Mass."

The busy bishop, then, who faces two or three Confirmation ceremonies on a given day could merely preside over the Mass much in the way he presides over benediction of the Blessed Sacrament. That would significantly ease the burden.

Secondly, the ritual, as we have also already observed, states that "in case of true necessity and special reason, for example, the large number of persons to be confirmed, the minister of confirmation . . . may associate other priests with himself in the administration of this sacrament."

The Confirmation time problem centers around the actual anointing rite. With a few assistants (the pastor, associates, priests present for the ceremony), the bishop should find this particular task much easier and certainly faster.

"Attention should be paid," says the Introduction, "to the festive and solemn character of the liturgical service." I know of nothing which could add festivity and solemnity to Confirmation as much as its celebration within Mass.

From the Acts of the Apostles (2:1-21)

When the day of Pentecost came it found them gathered in one place. Suddenly from up in the sky there came a noise like a strong, driving wind which was heard all through the house where they were seated. Tongues as of fire appeared, which parted and came to rest on each of them. All were filled with the Holy Spirit. They began to express themselves in foreign tongues and make bold proclamation as the Spirit prompted them.

Staying in Jerusalem at the time were devout Jews of every nation under heaven. These heard the sound, and assembled in a large crowd. They were much confused because each one heard these men speaking his own language. The whole occurrence astonished them. They asked in utter amazement, "Are not all of these men who are speaking Galileans? How is it that each of us hears them in his native tongue? We are Parthians, Medes, and Elamites. We live in Mesopotamia, Judea and Cappadocia, Pontus, the province of Asia, Phrygia and Pamphylia, Egypt, and the regions of Libya around Cyrene. There are even visitors from Rome—all Jews, or those who have come over to Judaism; Cretans and Arabs too. Yet each of us hears them speaking in his own tongue about the marvels God has accomplished." They were dumbfounded, and could make nothing at all of what had happened.

"What does this mean?" they asked one another, while a few remarked with a sneer, "They have had too much new wine!"

Peter stood up with the Eleven, raised his voice, and addressed them: "You are Jews indeed all of you staying in Jerusalem! Listen to what I have to say. You must realize that these men are not drunk, as you seem to think. It is only nine in the morning! No, it is what Joel the prophet spoke of:

It shall come to pass in the last days, says God,
  that I will pour out a portion of my spirit
    on all mankind:
Your sons and daughters shall prophesy,
  your young men shall see visions
  and your old men shall dream dreams.
Yes, even on my servants and handmaids
  I will pour out a portion of my spirit in
    those days,
  and they shall prophesy.
I will work wonders in the heavens above
  and signs on the earth below:
  blood, fire, and a cloud of smoke.
The sun shall be turned to darkness and the
    moon to blood
  before the coming of that great and glorious
    day of the Lord.
Then shall everyone be saved who calls on the
    name of the Lord.

From the

APOSTOLIC CONSTITUTION
on the
SACRAMENT OF CONFIRMATION

Paul, Bishop
Servant of the Servants of God
For an Everlasting Memorial

The sharing in the divine nature which is granted to men through the grace of Christ has a certain likeness to the origin, development, and nourishing of natural life. The faithful are born anew by baptism, strengthened by the sacrament of confirmation, and finally are sustained by the food of eternal life in the eucharist. By means of these sacraments of Christian initiation, they thus receive in increasing measure the treasures of divine life and advance towards the perfection of charity. It has rightly been written: "The body is washed, that the soul may be cleansed; the body is anointed, that the soul may be consecrated; the body is signed, that the soul too may be fortified; the body is overshadowed by the laying on of hands, that the soul too may be enlightened by the Spirit; the body is fed on the body and blood of Christ, that the soul too should be nourished by God."

The Second Vatican Ecumenical Council, conscious of its pastoral purpose, devoted special attention to these sacraments of initiation. It prescribed that the rites should be suitably revised in order to make them more suited to the understanding of the faithful. Since the Rite for the Baptism of Children, *revised at the mandate of that General Council and published at our command, is already in use, it is now fitting to publish the rite of confirmation, in order to show in its true light the unity of Christian initiation.*

In fact, careful attention and application have been devoted in these last years to the task of revising the manner of celebrating this sacrament. The aim of this work has been that "the intimate connection which this sacrament has with the whole of Christian initiation should be more lucidly set forth." The link between confirmation and the other sacraments of initiation is shown forth more clearly not only by closer association of these sacraments but also by the rite and words by which confirmation is conferred. This is done so that the rite and words of this sacrament may "express more clearly the holy things which they signify. The Christian people, so far as possible, should be able to understand them with ease and as a community to take full and active part in the celebration."

For that purpose, it has been our wish also to include in this revision what concerns the very essence of the rite of confirmation, through which the faithful receive the Holy Spirit as a Gift.

The New Testament shows how the Holy Spirit assisted Christ in fulfilling his messianic mission. On receiving the baptism of John, Jesus saw the Spirit descending on him (cf. Mark 1:10) and remaining with him (cf. John 1:32). He was impelled by the Spirit to undertake his public ministry as the Messiah, relying on the Spirit's presence and assistance. Teaching the people of Nazareth, he insinuated by what he said that the words of Isaiah, "The Spirit of the Lord is upon me," referred to himself (cf. Luke 4: 17-21).

He later promised his disciples that the Holy Spirit would help them also to bear fearless witness to their faith even before persecutors (cf. Luke 12:12). The day before he suffered, he assured his Apostles that he would send the Spirit of truth from his Father (cf. John 15:26) to stay with them "forever" (John 14:16) and help them to be his witnesses (cf. John 15:26). Finally, after his resurrection, Christ promised the coming descent of the Holy Spirit: "You will receive power when the Holy Spirit comes down on you; then you are to be my witnesses" (Acts 1:8; cf. Luke 24:49).

And in fact, on the day of the feast of Pentecost, the Holy Spirit came down in an extraordinary way on the Apostles as they were gathered together with Mary the Mother of Jesus and the group of disciples. They were so "filled with" the Holy Spirit (Acts 2:4) that by divine inspiration they began to proclaim "the mighty works of God." Peter regarded the Spirit who had thus come down upon the Apostles as the gift of the messianic age (cf. Acts 2:17-18). Those who believed the Apostles' preaching were then baptized and they too received "the gift of the Holy Spirit" (Acts 2:38). From that time on the Apostles, in fulfillment of Christ's wish, imparted to the neophytes the gift of the Spirit, by the laying on of hands to complete the grace of baptism. Hence it is that the Letter to the Hebrews lists among the first elements of Christian instruction the teaching about baptisms and the laying on of hands (Hebrews 6:2). This laying on of hands is rightly recognized by Catholic tradition as the beginning of the sacrament of confirmation, which in a certain way perpetuates the pentecostal grace in the Church.

This makes clear the specific importance of confirmation for sacramental initiation by which the faithful "as members of the living Christ are incorporated into him and made like him through baptism and through confirmation and the eucharist." In baptism, neophytes receive forgiveness of sins, adoption as sons of God, and the character of Christ, by which they are made members of the Church and for the first time become sharers in the priesthood of their

Savior (cf. 1 Peter 2:5,9). Through the sacrament of confirmation, those who have been born anew in baptism receive the inexpressible Gift, the Holy Spirit himself, by which "they are endowed . . . with special strength." Moreover, having received the character of this sacrament, they are "bound more intimately to the Church" and "they are more strictly obliged to spread and defend the faith both by word and by deed as true witnesses of Christ." Finally, confirmation is so closely linked with the holy eucharist that the faithful, after being signed by holy baptism and confirmation, are incorporated fully into the body of Christ by participation in the eucharist.

. . .

DISCUSSION QUESTIONS

1. When do you think Confirmation should be administered: at infancy with Baptism, around the seventh or eighth grade, when the candidate reaches maturity (during college, before marriage, after high school)? Why?
2. Do you envision any problems having priests assist the bishop with Confirmation?
3. Suggest some steps to insure that young persons freely choose to be confirmed and do not automatically receive the sacrament at a particular age or in a determined class.
4. Confirmed persons bear witness to Christ and the Holy Spirit "before all the world and eagerly work for the building up of the body of Christ." What does that mean in specific, practical terms?

part 3 / the table of the lord

Breaking Real Bread

"Children, you must be careful not to let the host touch your teeth and never should you chew the very body of Jesus." Such stern warnings from sincere religion teachers preparing young children for first Communion were not unheard of a few years ago. Their explanations of the wafer's whiteness followed a similar theme. Since the sinless, all holy God is truly present in the Eucharist, we may use only spotless, immaculately white, pure hosts at the altar.

We probably cringe at those remarks now or even laugh at them. But they are understandable enough and proceeded logically from the theological emphasis in vogue at that time. We spoke of Mass and Holy Communion in terms of awe, loftiness, adoration. Christ came into our midst on the altar so we might adore and worship him. If we really believed, spiritual writers told us, we would creep up the aisle on our knees.

Papal teaching and conciliar documents over the past two decades have neither denied nor minimized this truth of the Real Presence. But they did bring into sharper focus the fact that our Lord instituted the Mass as a sacrificial meal at his Last Supper. They also clarified the concept that Jesus gave up his body to eat and blood to drink under the sign of food. The materials for the Eucharist, therefore, should both be and look like bread and wine.

The second chapter of the *General Instruction* to the Roman Missal treats of "Requisites for Celebrating

Mass." Number 283 gives on this subject some interesting principles which contain quite practical implications.

"The nature of the sign demands that the material for the eucharistic celebration appear as actual food. The eucharistic bread, even though unleavened, should therefore be made in such a way that the priest can break it and distribute the parts to at least some of the faithful. When the number of communicants is large or other pastoral needs require it, small hosts may be used. The gesture of the 'breaking of the bread,' as the Eucharist was called in apostolic times, will more clearly show the Eucharist as a sign of unity and charity, since the one bread is being distributed among the members of one family."

One wonders if the paper-thin, tasteless, necessarily white hosts commonly employed today fulfill those requirements. What seems needed are larger, more substantial altar breads capable of division into perhaps two dozen particles for distribution to all the community at a weekday Mass or a celebration of similar circumstances. Obviously, smaller ones prepared in advance would still be a necessity for Sunday services and occasions when large numbers gather to worship. Large or small, however, these hosts should possess more substance to them and demand a real eating on the part of the communicating person.

Shortly after my arrival in Fulton, New York, as pastor of Holy Family Church, I obtained a recipe from an area Benedictine monastery for its large, whole-wheat altar breads. I then enlisted the aid of several ladies in the parish and asked them to try their hand at baking these for Sunday Mass. Initial efforts were not that successful; after a few further attempts, however, they came up with what I thought was a reasonably edible product.

We introduced these one Sunday, but, unfortunately, without sufficient explanation and warning. The results were not too bad—we only anointed ten people at Communion time who choked trying to swallow these one-half-inch-thick, square chunks. I should mention, in addition, that about 50 adults also canceled their parish envelopes after Mass. Other than those minor objections and difficulties . . .

A local baker several months later came to the rescue and developed the formula which you will find at the end of this chapter. He held a training session for the three women who do our baking, obtained some special flour, and guided them as they tried again. The product proved much better—tastier, softer, more like real bread and usually free of the inner, uncooked quality characteristic of our earlier hosts.

These are employed on both weekdays (almost exclusively) and Sundays (mainly). Those who communicate during the week find that receiving under both kinds, as is our custom, helps in consuming these particles. Sunday parishioners who find difficulties of any type with the new hosts usually wait until the last moment when the priests, having exhausted the supply of newer breads, completes distribution with the older kind of white, circular, thin wafers.

The people's reactions are mixed, I am sure. However, I have heard some positive comments from individuals who in the beginning did not like the change, yet now find these breads an improvement. In addition, use of such hosts has significant teaching impact ("We though many are one" and the "breaking of the bread" notions). Furthermore, we as priests find an occasional return to the older wafers a real letdown.

One point, however, becomes ever clearer—the Church's wish that we develop such altar breads seems to imply that Communion in the hand will once again and soon be commonplace. It is extremely awkward to distribute these new type hosts on the tongue. Placing them in the hand would be easier, faster, more hygienic and more reverent.

Drinking from the Chalice

We see lay persons today with ever-increasing frequency at Mass drinking our Lord's Precious Blood from the chalice. The American bishops have extended the occasions when Communion might be received under both kinds. These encompass almost any situation in which it can be done reverently and would prove spiritually helpful for the congregation.

The revised Roman Missal noted 14 acceptable situations including, for example, weddings, ordinations and retreats. A later instruction from the Congregation for Divine Worship gave to episcopal conferences in each country authority to enlarge upon that listing. Our own hierarchy responded to this quite liberally, citing these circumstances as appropriate for Communion from the cup, if the local bishop so decides: for all present on those special occasions enumerated in the Roman Missal, at funeral Masses and Eucharists for a special family observance, on days of special religious or civil significance for people of the United States, at the liturgies of Holy Thursday and the Easter Vigil, and during weekday Masses.

Why this restoration of an ancient practice? Vatican II gives the answer: That the fullness of sign in the eucharistic banquet may be more clearly seen by the faithful. Texts and rites, according to article 21, should be reformed to "express more clearly the holy things which they signify." The Church has always upheld Communion under the appearance of bread *and* wine as the ideal, as the most perfect way of sharing in the Eucharist. It more accurately speaks to us about the Blessed Sacrament, it more completely conveys the meaning of the Mass, it is the fuller, better sign.

A few illustrations to prove this point:

The Eucharist is a special, festive, joyful banquet. Christians celebrate in the context of a sacred meal Jesus' and our resurrection from sin and death. We naturally use bread for a meal, but wine, particularly in our culture, adds a dimension of specialness, festivity, rejoicing to the dinner. The Psalmist (Ps 104: 15) says: "wine to make them cheerful, oil to make them happy, and bread to make them strong." Check, also, Psalm 22: 5; Judges 9: 13; Proverbs 9: 2 for further references about wine's joy-making power.

Our Mass has deep roots in the Passover meal, a ritual ceremony in which the drink was spaced out and accompanied by brief prayers or explanations. In 1 Corinthians 10:16 we read: "the blessing-cup that we bless is a communion with the blood of Christ."

Jesus linked wine and cup in a unique way to his Second Coming, his final victorious triumph. "I shall not drink any more wine until the day I drink the new wine in the kingdom of God" (Mk 14:25; see also, Lk 22: 16-18; I Cor 11:26).

Christ instituted the Eucharist as a meal, but a distinctively sacrificial one. "My Body which will be given up for you," a priest proclaims during the eucharistic prayer. However, the chalice blessing expands on this: "the Blood of the new and everlasting covenant." It reveals Old and New Testament images (Ex 24: 8; Is 53) of an agreement between God and man, both sealed in blood.

Granted the ideal of Communion from the cup and its excellence in fully expressing the Eucharist's nature we must recognize certain difficulties connected with its use. Individuals, for several reasons, may object and large crowds can render distribution under both kinds awkward, even destructive of good worship.

Individuals and congregations in such cases should always feel free to receive only under the sign of bread. For the Council of Trent emphatically taught that Christ whole and entire and the true sacrament are also received under one species alone.

Parents and First Communion

"Nancy, how many gods are there? How many persons in God? Can you tell me the name of God's son when he came down on earth? His mother's name? Where was he born? Who comes into your heart when you receive Holy Communion? What does he look like and taste like? Is it really bread? Who is it?"

Nancy is a pretty, freckle-faced little first-grader in our parish. She had come with her maternal grandmother (the mother died suddenly last summer) to the rectory for an "interview" before first Communion and was sitting beside me in one of the parlor chairs while I asked these simple questions.

Before this spring visit, however, my tiny caller had carefully worked through a *Take and Eat* booklet designed to involve both parents and children in preparing for the Eucharist. She had read the text, studied its handsome color photos, drawn a portrait of her family, scrawled in big letters the name she received at Baptism, pasted to the appropriate page pictures of people celebrating, and sketched an illustration of how she in practice loves people.

My delightful task was to flip through the pages with Nancy, to ask for an explanation of her art work, to listen while she made the sign of the cross and recited from memory the Our Father, then to pose a few questions similar to the ones above.

Her birthday this year falls on a Sunday and soon she will receive the Lord for the first time on that day with her brothers and sisters. Later on she will also join our Solemn Parish First Communion Celebration, a May event designed to bring out the truth that the Eucharist has a wider, church-family dimension in addition to its obvious, personal, family significance.

"Barney, let's read the title of this big black book. That's right, 'Baptismal Register, Holy Family Church.' Can you find yourself in the index here? Page 37. Okay . . . there we are. Now point to the spot which says Barney Joseph Naioti. What is your birthday? Your date of Baptism? The name of your father and your mother? Your godparents? The priest who baptized you?"

This was another "interview," with a young boy, obviously, and one in the second grade. He, like Nancy, had been baptized in the church where he was about to make his first Communion (a less frequent occurrence these days) and it gave us an excellent opportunity to show the intimate connection between these two sacraments of initiation.

Earlier in the week a father and mother brought their two children, both boys, for the workbook review and a few simple inquiries. In this case, however, they had received Baptism in other churches. Each child, consequently, carried instead a plain white envelope with his name printed unevenly in large red crayon letters across the front. The necessary baptismal document was enclosed. We carefully looked at the records and talked individually about their meaning with the youngsters.

Such a parental involvement program was a radical innovation for our parish, although a familiar pattern now in most forward-thinking churches. We ran into some early objections: "Why the change? This is the priest's or the sisters' job. Isn't that the purpose of Catholic schools? We're not really qualified."

However, gentle, but firm encouragement and further explanation from the pulpit plus, especially, small group meetings at several homes of participating parents seemed to dissipate fears and reassure hesitant fathers or mothers.

I personally found the rectory visit or interview with each child an invaluable part of this program. It does take time and presupposes in the priest a certain ease with such boys and girls. However, that ten- or 15-minute encounter can bind parish, priest, parent and child even more tightly together. Mother and dad naturally are nervous, wondering how well they have taught their child and if their offspring will respond properly. The children naturally are excited at this attention, the new surroundings, a "father" who checks their books and speaks with them about God, Jesus, Baptism, and Holy Communion.

One father's comment afterwards probably best summarizes the kind of positive effect this meeting produces. "I'm a nervous person in situations like these. But when the boys were answering those questions, particularly the younger one, I cried. It just did something to me inside, made me feel very, very proud."

First Confession and First Communion

A few springs ago I listened for an hour to the initial confessions of young boys and girls about to make their first Holy Communion on a Saturday several days later. The experience simply confirmed a conviction I have held for many years: The practice of mandatory and group confession before tiny tots begin to receive the Eucharist should be changed.

We took all the proper steps suggested to reduce these children's fears about the confessional and to make the sacrament a beautiful, happy, peace-giving encounter with the God of mercy. We turned lights on within the "box," ran the little ones through a "practice confession," moved the slide back and forth, showed them the priest's section, and, most importantly, spoke about Jesus and his love for us.

Still, many felt afraid, both before and afterwards.

My own reservations about the value of these procedures come more from a dozen years' work as priest in charge of the parish first Communion class than from pure academic research. That personal reluctance to insist on confession for children in grades one or two before they receive the Blessed Sacrament is shared, I believe, by the vast majority of nuns who, after all, generally care for most of the catechesis involved.

I base my assertion on some data from the Portland, Maine, diocese. During a liturgical workshop for sisters at Bangor in the early 60's, a local moderator of the session asked the 200 participants how many preferred to see first Confession delayed until after first Communion. All but one of the nuns raised their hands.

This clear testimony and my strong conviction hinge on these fundamental points: It is almost psychologically impossible for youngsters at that age level to commit mortal sins and, consequently, they have no obligation to approach the sacrament of Penance before Communion; furthermore, while devotional confessions can carry certain benefits even for small children, the potentially harmful effects seem to far outweigh the possible advantages.

Archbishop Cousins of Milwaukee established in September of 1970 certain guidelines for first Confession and first Communion which typify what has now become the more common practice in this country. I certainly welcome them and know the sisters in Maine would see these norms as a fulfillment of hopes expressed in that conference a decade ago.

—A child may be permitted to receive first Communion in first or second grade.

—It is the responsibility of parents together with the pastor and the catechist to determine when the child is ready to receive this sacrament.

—The sacrament of Penance need not precede the reception of first Communion. Confession at an early age could open the door to the danger of legalism and confession without conversion.

—A progression of catechesis on Penance will be a part of the religious education of all children. In the primary grades, children will receive a simple initiation into the meaning of the virtue of penance. In the middle grades, children should receive the sacrament of Penance in a communal setting. In addition, opportunities for private auricular confessions should be made available to the child during these years.

—Private confession opportunities may also be provided for individual children at an earlier date, if pastorally necessary or desirable.

Parish First Communion

Over half of our young boys and girls made first Communion twice this year. The initial occasion was on a Sunday of their choice. Each boy or girl on that date and during a regularly scheduled Mass came to the altar flanked by mom and dad. The second time occurred on Pentecost as we celebrated a Solemn Parish First Communion for 64 children who took this next step on the path toward full membership in the Christian community.

A family first Communion underscores the parents' essential role in preparing children for reception of the Eucharist. We offered that as an option, and, after a bit of beginning resistance or reluctance, nearly 30 families, surprisingly enough, selected this alternative.

Our Solemn Parish First Communion sought to stress the concept that Christian initiation involves several stages—Baptism, Confirmation and the Eucharist. It also tried to illustrate the truth that the Christian community, symbolized by a congregation gathered for the 8:30 Sunday liturgy, welcomes those young ones more fully into its midst.

Planners of the liturgical service, wishing to convey these principles through the celebration itself, involved a dozen or more of the boys and girls as readers, gift bearers, and leaders for the sign of peace. The children did beautifully.

Anita Pappalardo and Bobbie Yager stepped up from the pews at the appropriate times (with some verbal encouragement from the celebrant) to proclaim the first two scriptural excerpts. They stood by the presidential chair next to the priest and read quite well from a typed script edited from the biblical passages assigned for Pentecost. We dropped a few sentences from Reading 1, judging that tiny tots shouldn't really be expected to pronounce Mesopotamia, Cappadocia, Phrygia, Pamphylia and Elamites. There was absolute silence throughout the church as Anita and Bobbie spoke God's word to his people.

The celebrant carried on a dialogue homily with the class in the manner suggested for Confirmation by the revised Roman rite. When asked if they thought the boys and girls were ready for the Eucharist, parents, relatives and other adults present responded "yes" through their applause.

Two boys and two girls led the congregation in a brief prayer of the faithful. "That people in the world will stop fighting . . . For our fathers and mothers who helped us get ready for first Holy Communion . . . That the strike at the chocolate factory may soon come to an end . . . For people who are sick and those who are old, that God may take care of them, let us pray to the Lord."

In addition to the water, wine, hosts and money offerings, representatives of the class brought forward at presentation time a candle (recalling Baptism) and a book (recalling the workbook completed by each child before his or her interview with the parish clergy).

Six first communicants walked from their places to the sanctuary for the sign of peace and received from the concelebrating priests their gesture of reconciliation. They then carried the message and handshake down central aisles of the church, stopping at the end of each pew and wishing worshipers, "Peace be with you."

We discovered by accident an important principle to be followed, in our judgment, during the catechesis and preparation process: Don't overrehearse. With parental involvement in the teaching process, a personal interview by the clergy beforehand, and some general training in the parochial school or religious education classes, repeated practice sessions seem unnecessary, even unwise.

Two Saturday morning rehearsals of one hour's duration proved adequate. More significantly, the boys and girls came to church on that Sunday morning reverent, but relaxed; orderly, but not uptight; aware, but not anxious. We felt this procedure freed them from hang-ups about externals and enabled them to concentrate on essentials.

. . .

From the Roman Missal's General Instruction

48. *(3) The breaking of the one bread is a sign of the unity of the faithful, and in communion they receive the body and blood of Christ as the Apostles did from his hands.*

56. *(c)* The breaking of bread: *this gesture of Christ at the Last Supper gave the entire eucharistic action its name in apostolic times. In addition to its practical aspect, it signifies that in communion we who are many are made one body in the one bread which is Christ (1 Cor 10:17).*

240. The sign of communion is more complete when given under both kinds, since the sign of the eucharistic meal appears more clearly. The intention of Christ that the new and eternal covenant be ratified in his blood is better expressed, as is the relation of the eucharistic banquet to the heavenly banquet.

From the Addendum to the General Catechetical Directory

"Having weighed all these points, and keeping in mind the common and general practice which per se cannot be derogated without the approval of the Apostolic See, and also having heard the Conferences of Bishops, the Holy See judges it fitting that the practice now in force in the Church of putting Confession ahead of first Communion should be retained. This in no way prevents this custom from being carried out in various ways, as, for instance, by having a communal penitential celebration precede or follow the reception of the sacrament of Penance.

"The Holy See is not unmindful of the special conditions that exist in various countries, but it exhorts the bishops in this important matter not to depart from the practice in force without having first entered into communication with the Holy See in a spirit of hierarchical communion. Nor should they in any way allow the pastors or educators or religious institutes to begin or to continue to abandon the practice in force.

"In regions, however, where new practices have already been introduced which depart notably from the pristine practice, the Conferences of Bishops will wish to submit these experiments to a new examination. If after that they wish to continue these experiments for a longer time, they should not do so unless they have first communicated with the Holy See, which will willingly hear them, and they are at one mind with the Holy See."

DISCUSSION QUESTIONS

1. Discuss the pros and cons of first Confession before or after first Communion.

2. "Preparing children for first Communion is the priests' and sisters' job. That's why we send our kids to Catholic school and to CCD classes. We're not qualified." Comment on this response.

3. As an experiment, bake some altar breads according to the following recipe.

. . .

RECIPE FOR UNLEAVENED BREAD

3 cups whole wheat flour
3 cups high-gluten flour
3 level tablespoons granulated sugar
1 pinch of salt
2 oz. shortening
1 tablespoon molasses
2⅔ cups of lukewarm water

Combine and blend all above ingredients *except water.* When ingredients are well blended, add water and mix lightly with fingers until dough is sticky.

Place dough on floured surface and form into shape of loaf of bread.

Then slice off pieces of dough approximately 3 oz. each.

Pat each piece of dough to form desired shape.

Score each circle of dough to yield number of pieces desired.

Place on ungreased cookie sheet.

Bake 16-18 minutes each side in moderate oven 375°.

Yields approximately 21 hosts.

part 4 / peace for the troubled sinner

Confession in the Seventies

"With all these changes in the liturgy, are there any plans to modify the sacrament of Penance? Will Confession be changed or eliminated in the seventies? These questions come up consistently during the discussion period after lectures on liturgical renewal.

Will we see the prayers and forgiveness formula altered? Yes, perhaps soon. Will the Holy See ever establish, as standard practice, group absolution without private mention of personal sins to a specific priest? Very unlikely. Will the type of Confession we have known and observed over the past decades be prohibited or discouraged? No.

This writer certainly would welcome improved texts and a clearer procedure for use by the priest and the penitent in this sacrament. We should also renovate confessional "boxes" and develop comfortable rooms for optional face to-face encounters. But I wonder if our fundamental problem here is not the form we follow or the place we use, but the approach we take. I wonder if forward-thinking religion instructors have not too quickly written off private telling of sins as another once valuable, but now outmoded teaching of the Catholic Church. I wonder if the field ripe for the harvest at the present moment is not in fact a positive, growth-oriented course for young and old alike on "How to make a good confession."

Similar comments came recently from the lips of a pretty and personable coed. She is neither a future nun nor a careless Catholic. Even as a busy nursing student she finds time occasionally to pray her rosary and stop in for weekday Mass. This young lady's question basically is: "Why go when I haven't failed God seriously? Why slip in and out of the box without any real change in my life? What good are routine confessions?" And, like many in the Church today, she allows months to pass from one confession to the next.

The problem then seems to revolve around devotional use of the sacrament. Those who feel they have severed friendship with the Lord by serious sin and seek reconciliation experience their own difficulties with Confession. Courage is what they need, and a willingness to leave the past behind. The person, however, who leads an essentially good life, but wishes to improve it, who tries, but would like to do better can or should see Penance as a very helpful instrument in this struggle to grow.

To help people make devotional confessions richer and less routine, Father John E. Corrigan several years ago wrote a little pamphlet, *Bless Me, Father,* as a "guide to Confession for men and women of today, with advice on the examination of conscience and practical examples." I presume both author's and publisher's permissions (Claretian Publications, 221 West Madison Street, Chicago, Illinois 60606, Pamphlet Department) to excerpt the following sample confession of a housewife. It illustrates a constructive examination of conscience, a painful but healing admission of lesser sins and a specific, positive approach to resolutions for improvements.

"My last confession was two weeks ago. I am a housewife and mother of two small children. My resolution for the last few months has been to curb my tendency to nag my husband and be more cheerful with him. I think I did better during this period.

"I have incurred unnecessary debts and have managed the home finances poorly and selfishly.

"I learned last week that I am pregnant, and I have been depressed and felt resentful because it was unexpected. I think I have overcome these feelings now.

"I am only gradually adjusting to our new neighborhood. I find it hard to meet people and I have been lacking in friendliness with my new neighbors.

"My Lenten resolution to read the New Testament every day has suffered because of the company we had last week. I'll begin again."

. . .

A woman who had seen this hypothetical housewife's confession in one of my columns, swiftly responded "in the interest of justice and fair play" with her own, the sample confession of a husband which follows:

"My last confession was two weeks ago. I am a husband and the father of two small children. My resolution for the past few months has been to curb my tendency to punish my wife by walking around every day with a 'long face.'

"I often stop on my way home from work to have a few drinks; consequently, I am often late for supper. This understandably upsets my wife—as it would any woman—but when she attempts to discuss it, I maintain a stubborn and sullen silence.

"I learned last week that my wife is pregnant again. God forgive me! I yelled at her, as though it were her fault instead of mine. I continually force myself on her, insisting that she satisfy my sexual cravings whenever I demand it. I sense that some nights she is 'bone-tired' but I pretend not to notice. After all, I know my 'rights.'

"I think I have broken my wife's spirit. Forgive me, God. Forgive me. Forgive me. I fear it will be a long time before I can earn her forgiveness. . . ."

Young People and Confession

Are you confused about the issue of when first Confession should come in a young child's life? Or even ask the deeper question, why must we confess our sins to a priest? Or wonder how you can improve the quality of your own confessions?

Ave Maria Press has published *I Confess: The Sacrament of Penance Today,* by Father Francis Buckley, a small book which should help you resolve some of those matters.

The author gives considerable attention in his work to young people and their confessions. Using data secured from psychological studies, he suggests different approaches which could make the sacrament of Penance more effective for children at different age levels. One Friday, immediately after reading through galley sheets of the text, I tried out several of his ideas with a class of fourth-graders in the local Catholic school. They worked very well.

Buckley maintains children of 10 or 11 can grasp the notion that the priest in confession is like a father who wants to understand or like a doctor who wants to heal. They know neither will be able to understand or heal unless the symptoms of the illness or trouble are fully described. As a consequence, he recommends they analyze sample adult confessions and learn from them how to better their own.

He offers and I used with our boys and girls the following example:

"Forgive me, Father, I'm a married man. It's been a month since my last confession. I got angry and lost my temper with the children. This happens often now when I get home from work. I'm tired and I don't want to be bothered.

"I know this is selfish. My anger just makes things worse. I'll try to spend more time with the kids and listen to them instead of yell. Where should I start? Have you any advice?"

With but little assistance, our youngsters quickly came to the key conclusion desired. They recognized the married man not only related "what" he had done, but, perhaps more importantly, "why" he had so acted, and then sought advice as to "how" he could improve.

Father Buckley later states that when children begin to capture the feel of confessions made in this fashion, they can profit from role-playing exercises in which one takes the part of a priest and another acts as the penitent. Two of my students swiftly volunteered for the confessor's role, but they all verbally and visually said "no" when I sought actors for the penitent's part. Finally, under pressure, Jimmy Borek agreed to confess (he really wanted to be the priest) and David Gillard heard his tale of sins.

Jimmy made a brief confession. "I'm married and I got angry at my wife." "Father" Gillard's counseling efforts were just as limited. "You shouldn't do that. You're supposed to love her and be nice to her."

The experience was a serious-funny event for both the class and for the two performers. Everyone laughed—the class, the two boys, the observing teacher and the experimenting priest who started it all. But I think these young people learned a bit about good confessions through the role-playing exercise and I plan to repeat this after school resumes in the fall.

The author of *I Confess* believes children of this age appreciate penances designed in a special way for them and points out that if the confessor can't think of an imaginative one, he might ask the child.

Buckley once inquired of a little girl what she would like to do to make up with her mother. "I'd like to bake a cake," she replied. After verifying she could in fact produce one and that this would please her mother, he said, "All right, as a penance bake that cake for your mother."

We could rightly ask, considering the potential kitchen mess, if this would be a penance for the child or for the mother.

An Upswing in Confessions

I haven't heard recently of many places with an upswing in Saturday confessions, but I do know about one. That parish is in Macon, Georgia, and its weekly bulletin describes the congregation: a community steeped in tradition but on the move in our modern world.

"St. Joseph's is the mother church of Middle Georgia. It served Catholics scattered from the Florida border to the mountains of Tennessee. Even the great metropolis of Atlanta was once its mission. Rich in history and strong in faith, St. Joseph's today is striving to keep alive the traditions of the past and give them a vitality in keeping with the exciting times in which we live."

Gray-haired and hardworking Father William Coleman shepherds this flock, aided by an associate pastor, Father Thomas Healy, "the young priest with the very black hair." They alternate hearing confessions at the customary 4:00-5:30 and 7:30-8:30 periods, but penitents know exactly who will be in the "box" at what hours. An announcement in the bulletin one week, for example, reads: "Confessions on Saturday will be heard in the afternoon by Father Healy and in the evening by Father Coleman." Moreover, each priest attaches a nameplate to the confessional during his own tour of duty.

At St. Joseph's, however, sinners kneel, not in a conventional box, but in the more comfortable setting of a confessional room. The carpeted and spacious area for the sacrament of Penance is actually a converted baptistry, a space made available when the pastor renovated this church and moved its font forward to the sanctuary. A partition within the room gives penitents the option of an anonymous, behind-the-screen arrangement or of an open, face-to-face encounter. In either case, the individual no longer must whisper, but can speak normally, yet with an assurance of secrecy.

Father Coleman has ordered a pamphlet rack for the confessional room, a shelf to contain appropriate literature for this sacrament. The priest will then be able easily to assign passages from these publications as penances or suggest particular booklets which complement his own words of advice. In addition, the pastor hopes soon an artist, through proper colors, symbols and paintings, may add to the room a special atmosphere radiating warmth, joy, forgiveness and peace.

Confessions are up in Macon, but not simply because of a change in the furniture. The clergy preach and teach about this subject, indicate a willingness to listen and help plan programs geared for the Christian growth of their parishioners. A few excerpts from the "Parish Programs" brochure illustrate what I mean:

"Confession—Confessions are regularly heard. . . . Many people prefer to spend a longer time than the regular hours allow. In this case call the rectory for an appointment for a counseling-type confession."

"Counseling—Any person wrestling with a problem will find in the parish priests someone very willing to listen and help discover possible solutions. In any time of need you are always welcome at St. Joseph's rectory."

"What is a parish? A parish is people—united at the altar in worship of God through his Son, Jesus. The most important thing we do is pray together. Yet, readying ourselves for prayer by a good life requires help. In many ways our parish program provides us with such help."

Just how much are confessions at St. Joseph's on the increase? According to Father Coleman, the parish formerly averaged a half-dozen penitents in the afternoon and again in the evening. Today the number has risen to about 25 on each occasion.

What kind of people come? The saved? Older persons? Traditionalists reverting to habits of earlier days? Some fit these categories, of course, but many have long hair or thick beards, wear beads or carry babies in their arms. They represent the younger, now generation. So much so that an elderly lady living nearby complained about the great crowd of "hippies" who drop into this Macon, Georgia, church every Saturday afternoon and evening.

Communal Penance Services: Theory

Local stores these days begin their "Christmas sell" long before Thanksgiving. The Church, however, still waits until Advent for its season of "joyful and spiritual expectation." We prepare, during that period, for the December 25 feast which recalls Jesus' coming in the past at Bethlehem and anticipates his glorious return at the end of time.

As a part of the Advent preparation process, more and more parishes throughout the United States have been conducting communal penance services. Those biblically oriented liturgies vary greatly in format and content. In essence, however, they seek to convey these points: God's constant love for sinful man, the social nature of sin, and the communal nature of forgiveness.

1. God's constant love for sinful man. Our Lord naturally will not forgive the unrepentant. He does not compel us to accept his love and mercy. Nevertheless, Jesus' love for men never stops and in a strange, mysterious manner his grace really starts the sinner's conversion. We tend to forget these comforting truths and often rely perhaps too much on our own initiative.

Penance services attempt to place the conversion-forgiveness experience in proper perspective. They bring out the need for a true change of heart and even specify in hard, concrete terms what repentance means in one's personal, practical life. But they likewise emphasize, especially through appropriate scriptural readings and an accompanying homily, the Lord's ever-ready willingness to pardon and grant peace.

The New York Archdiocesan Liturgical Commission's January, 1971, *Bulletin,* "Communal Penance Issue," included a series of such conversion-forgiveness texts from the bible suitable for these services. For example: Ezechiel 36, "I shall give you a new heart," John 8, "The adulterous woman," Luke 15, "The prodigal son." These and others have been incorporated into *Repent and Believe,* a booklet edited by Rev. William Freburger and published by Ave Maria Press.

It is expected that the revised rite for the sacrament of Penance to be issued in the not too distant future by the Holy See will contain a list of over 100 similar biblical references. Introductory principles of that Roman document encourage their use in penitential liturgies as a means of making the Lord present, of stirring up our faith, and/or reminding us that Jesus came, not to condemn, but to save sinners.

2. The social nature of sin. Every sin must, of necessity, come from the human heart and involve an individual person. But each moral failure touches others outside of and beyond ourselves. We need to understand that sin affects not only our relationship with God, but also with fellowmen and with the world around us.

To illustrate: Open battles in the home between bitter husbands and wives leave lasting scars on the children who witness them. Negligent or selfish vacationers and industries destroy forests and pollute streams. Unconcerned taxpayers or insensitive administrators may have indirectly contributed to the tragedy at Attica prison.

Through a group examination of conscience which asks carefully prepared, pointed questions, the communal penance service seeks to deepen the participant's awareness of just how far the impact of his or her sin can reach.

3. The communal nature of forgiveness. If sin ruptures our relationship with God, neighbor and the world, then forgiveness must involve reconciliation with all three. These innovative penance liturgies attempt to underscore this truth through congregational prayer, common penances and some concluding gesture of harmony or peace. The Our Father works particularly well in this context. "Forgive us our trespasses as we forgive those who trespass against us. . . ."

Communal Penance Services: Practice

Our before-Christmas common penance service opened with congregational singing of "Whatsoever You Do to the Least of My Brothers," included the traditional "Come Holy Ghost," and ended with music from "Jesus Christ Superstar."

A woman proclaimed the first scriptural selection, a man the second, and a married couple led the community in an examination of conscience by alternately reading appropriate passages from the Old Testament (Deuteronomy 5, Leviticus 19) and the New (Matthew 5, Mark 7).

This 45-minute ceremony also featured the TeleKETICS film on Penance (very, very excellent, moving many, perhaps most to tears), joint recitation of two psalms, a brief homily, and words or gestures of reconciliation and peace at the conclusion.

The questions and answers which follow guided us in our evaluation of the experiment and reflect views of both the planners and the participants.

Was it too long? Probably. The laity didn't object and one couldn't detect in the congregation the usual deadly signs of boredom—coughing, uneasiness, watch-glancing—but we felt it could have been slightly shortened. Omission of one reading with introductory remarks and its reflective pause would just about take care of that difficulty.

How successful? Moderately so. It attracted fewer than anticipated, although other factors (snow, shopping, basketball) may have interfered with attendance. However, there were enough to justify the effort, and those who worshiped that evening, as far as we could determine, generally found the service inspirational and a source of true spiritual renewal.

Did they become confused and wonder if this replaced Confession? Very definitely. A sermon on the preceding Sunday and the homily within the rite itself attempted to explain these points: Forgiveness of sins can come outside of Confession in many ways (e.g., reception of the Eucharist, works of charity); serious failures require submission to the priest in the context of Confession; Confession, even when not required, offers much to us in terms of grace and growth. But some in the coffee-and-cookie period after the service indicated by their conversation that they really hadn't grasped these notions.

Wouldn't general absolution within the ceremony solve that difficulty? I don't really think so. Apart from current Church legislation which prohibits this except in cases of emergency, it seems to me there are serious practical, pastoral reasons which make that unwise.

If mortal sin means a free, deep, total rejection of God's love and his plan for us, then is it sufficient for one guilty of this to be reconciled through a group communal rite, however beautiful and compelling? I have my doubts and the long tradition of the Church would seem to support me in that conviction. Moreover, if we believe that lesser sins can be forgiven outside Confession by sharing in something like a common penance service, then why complicate matters by interjecting an absolution formula within the ceremony?

Why not interrupt the rite, make sufficient priests available and have participants confess individually to them? This apparently is a frequent resolution of the problem. In it, the penitent skips the initial formula (bless me Father . . .), merely recites a list of sins and the confessor omits advice, counseling or other words tailored to needs of the specific person. All then normally complete a single, previously agreed upon penance.

I am not one to quibble with success—and this procedure does seem to enjoy considerable popularity—but I retain serious reservations about the practice. The confessor here becomes an absolving machine and, further, is in effect prohibited from any type of dialogue or discussion with the penitent should that seem desirable or necessary.

Anything which tends to interfere with the freedom of either the priest confessor or the person confessing has always made me most uncomfortable. I view this solution in that light and, in addition, see it forcing Confession into a false framework for the sake of giving participants the best of both worlds.

What did we do about Confession? We invited other priests over for the occasion and, following the service, offered those who wished this opportunity for individual confession of sins. Moreover, the ceremony didn't really conclude. After the gesture of peace and reconciliation the musicians (organ and guitar) played for about five minutes, creating an atmosphere in which those who attended either pondered what took place, moved toward the confessionals, or walked downstairs for refreshments.

The quiet sense of repentance and hope (not really an ebullient rejoicing) continued on and we were busy with confessions (fruitful ones I would add) for nearly an hour afterwards.

My overall impression? The common penance service serves an excellent purpose, should be conducted several times a year (e.g., Advent, Lent), complements Confession, but does not and ought not to replace it.

From the Book of Genesis, Chapter 3

Now the serpent was the most cunning of all the animals that the LORD God had made. The serpent asked the woman, "Did God really tell you not to eat from any of the trees in the garden?" The woman answered the serpent: "We may eat of the fruit of the trees in the garden; it is only about the fruit of the tree in the middle of the garden that God said, 'You shall not eat it or even touch it, lest you die.'" But the serpent said to the woman: "You certainly will not die! No, God knows well that the moment you eat of it your eyes will be opened and you will be like gods who know what is good and what is bad." The woman saw that the tree was good for food, pleasing to the eyes, and desirable for gaining wisdom. So she took some of its fruit and ate it; and she also gave some to her husband, who was with her, and he ate it. Then the eyes of both of them were opened, and they realized that they were naked; so they sewed fig leaves together and made loincloths for themselves.

When they heard the sound of the LORD God moving about in the garden at the breezy time of the day, the man and his wife hid themselves from the LORD God among the trees of the garden. The LORD God then called to the man and asked him, "Where are you?" He answered, "I heard you in the garden; but I was afraid, because I was naked, so I hid myself." Then he asked, "Who told you that you were naked? You have eaten, then, from the tree of which I had forbidden you to eat!" The man replied, "The woman whom you put here with me—she gave me fruit from the tree, and so I ate it." The LORD God then asked the woman, "Why did you do such a thing?" The woman answered, "The serpent tricked me into it, so I ate it."

Then the LORD God said to the serpent:

"Because you have done this,
you shall be banned from all the animals
and from all the wild creatures;
On your belly shall you crawl,
and dirt shall you eat all the days of your life.

I will put enmity between you and the woman,
and between your offspring and hers;
He will strike at your head,
while you strike at his heel."

To the woman he said:
"I will intensify the pangs of your childbearing;
in pain shall you bring forth children.
Yet your urge shall be for your husband,
and he shall be your master."

To the man he said: "Because you listened to your wife and ate from the tree of which I had forbidden you to eat,

"Cursed be the ground because of you!
In toil shall you eat its yield
all the days of your life.
Thorns and thistles shall it bring forth to you,
as you eat of the plants of the field.

By the sweat of your face
shall you get bread to eat,
Until you return to the ground,
from which you were taken;
For you are dirt,
and to dirt you shall return."

The man called his wife Eve, because she became the mother of all the living.

For the man and his wife the LORD God made

leather garments, with which he clothed them. Then the LORD God said: "See! The man has become like one of us, knowing what is good and what is bad! Therefore, he must not be allowed to put out his hand to take fruit from the tree of life also, and thus eat of it and live forever." The LORD God therefore banished him from the garden of Eden, to till the ground from which he had been taken. When he expelled the man, he settled him east of the garden of Eden; and he stationed the cherubim and the fiery revolving sword to guard the way to the tree of life.

. . .

From the Encyclical Letter of Pope Pius XII on the Mystical Body of Christ

The same result would follow the opinions of those who assert that little importance should be given to the frequent confession of venial sins. Of far greater importance, they say, is that general confession which the spouse of Christ surrounded by her children in the Lord makes each day by the mouth of the priest as he approaches the altar. It is true indeed, venerable brothers, that venial sins may be expiated in many ways which are to be highly commended. But to hasten daily progress along the path of virtue we wish the pious practice of frequent confession to be earnestly advocated. Not without the inspiration of the Holy Spirit was this practice introduced into the Church. By it genuine self-knowledge is increased, Christian humility is developed, bad habits are corrected, spiritual neglect and tepidity are countered, the conscience is purified, the will is strengthened, salutary self-control is obtained, and an increase of grace is secured by the very fact that the sacrament is received. Let those, therefore, among the younger clergy who make light of or weaken esteem for frequent confession realize that what they are doing is foreign to the Spirit of Christ, and disastrous for the mystical body of our Savior.

. . .

From the *Constitution on the Sacred Liturgy* of Vatican II

72. The rite and formulas for the sacrament of penance are to be revised so that they more clearly express both the nature and effect of the sacrament.

. . .

From the June 16, 1972, Decree from the Sacred Congregation for the Doctrine of the Faith on *Pastoral Norms Concerning the Administration of General Sacramental Absolution*

"Christ our Lord instituted the Sacrament of Penance in order that the faithful who have sinned might obtain pardon from the mercy of God for the offences committed against him and at the same time be reconciled with the Church (cf. Lumen Gentium, *11). He instituted it when he gave the Apostles and their lawful successors the power to forgive and retain sins (cf. Jn 20:22-23)."*

"The Council of Trent solemnly taught that for full and perfect forgiveness of sins three acts are required from the penitent as parts of the sacrament, these acts being contrition, confession and satisfaction. It also taught that absolution is given by the priest, who acts as judge, and that it is necessary by divine law to confess to a priest each and every mortal sin and the circumstances that alter the species of sins that are remembered after a careful examination of conscience."

"The teaching of the Council of Trent must be firmly held and faithfully put into practice. This implies a

reprobation of the recent custom which has sprung up in places by which there is a presumption to satisfy the precept of sacramentally confessing mortal sins for the purpose of obtaining absolution by confession made only generally or through what is called a community celebration of penance. This reprobation is demanded not only by divine precept as declared by the Council of Trent, but also by the very great good of souls deriving, according to centuries-long experience, from individual confession rightly administered. Individual and integral confession and absolution remain the only ordinary way for the faithful to be reconciled to God and the Church unless physical or moral impossibility excuses from such confession."

"The faithful are carefully to be taught that liturgical celebrations and community rites of penance are of great usefulness for the preparation of a more fruitful confession of sins and amendment of life. Care must however be taken that such celebrations or rites are not confused with sacramental confession and absolution."

DISCUSSION QUESTIONS

1. "Why must I confess to another human being, to an individual, to a priest? Can't I go to God alone for forgiveness of my sins?" How would you respond to this common objection?
2. Have you found the "box" an obstacle to a good Confession? What do you think about a confessional room? About face-to-face Confessions?
3. Read the account from Genesis above and see what it teaches about the social dimension of sin. Then conceive some current examples of how a person's sin touches many others and a few possible ways of reconciling the injured parties.

part 5 / a liturgy for lovers

To Live in Love

A columnist and film critic for the Los Angeles *Times* wrote recently about "A Mess of Movies Look at the Mess of Marriage." The title spread carried photos of a half dozen stars with this caption: "A gallery of actresses cope with miseries of matrimony in new films. Their woes include boredom, suffocation and husbands who are frustrated, overworked, inert, unfaithful or all four."

In his opening paragraph the Hollywood writer observed:

> Having spent more than half a century persuading us that an endless succession of Theys lived happily ever after, the movies almost as one have now coughed nervously, toed the deep-pile wall-to-wall carpet, averted our gaze and confessed that that isn't quite the whole story.
>
> In fact, it's hard to remember a recent movie which dared to suggest that the couple would live happily through next weekend, let alone ever after. Like our society, the movies are taking a hard and worried look at marriage, weighing it and finding it less wanted than it used to be.

Young marriageable persons know, unfortunately,

that *The Graduate* and *Bob & Carol & Ted & Alice*, for example, are not mere dream concoctions of the cinema, but painful slices of real life. High and rising divorce rates plus the marital misery of many who still live together but no longer love each other, trouble those ready for Matrimony. They wonder what happened to these people along the way and question if the same thing will occur in their lives. Engaged couples love deeply, but in the face of such harsh evidence they legitimately ask if the love is real and will last, if the risk is worth it, if they will find happiness and bliss in marriage or discover bitterness and hell on earth.

Richard Dali and Jerilyn Jerry viewed those movies, weighed these alternatives and then vowed, on May 16, 1970, in St. Thomas of Canterbury Church at Cornwall-on-Hudson, New York, to be true in good times and in bad, in sickness and in health, promised to love and honor each other all the days of their lives.

Like hundreds of couples in the United States this spring and summer, Jeri and Dick planned their own wedding ceremony, picked out the readings, prayers, and blessings, produced a program booklet for the guests. A paragraph of welcome in this leaflet set the tone for a warm and personal service which involved the entire congregation. "We would like to welcome you, our friends, to share with us this, our most beautiful day; to witness, and be part of, the beginning of our lives together."

The pastor of St. Thomas helped. An admiral in the Navy and former chief of chaplains, Msgr. George R. Rosso several months earlier had purchased a handsome silver cup with handles specifically designed for use at nuptial Masses. It seems to work particularly well. Normally bride and groom gingerly raise chalice to their lips and consume but a drop or two of the Lord's Precious Blood. I found the couple more relaxed and comfortable holding Msgr. Rosso's unique "loving cup" and better disposed to drink Christ's blood instead of merely sipping it.

Some parish priests (Father John Beno in Pueblo, Colorado, comes to my mind) obtain a similar, but ceramic cup for the wedding and present it to husband and wife as a gift after the nuptial Mass. They are encouraged to reserve it for the anniversary each year as a reminder of that covenant ratified in Jesus' blood on the first day of their wedded life.

Richard and Jerilyn were anxious that friends and relatives might share in the joy and love of "our most beautiful day." In this the young lovers were following the intent of the revised ritual which states: "At the words 'Let us offer each other the sign of peace,' the married couple and all present show their peace and love for one another in an appropriate way." They felt the sign of peace would be an excellent opportunity to communicate love, joy, and harmony, especially at a time when the nation is split by hatred and violence.

After the nuptial blessing they embraced, then communicated a greeting of peace to the celebrant. Next, the groom walked to his brother, the best man, shook hands and said, "Peace be with you, Sam." The bride stepped to her sister, the maid of honor, kissed this college senior and whispered, "Barbara, may peace be with you." The priest, at their request, addressed those in the pews with these words. "Dick and Jeri obviously are very much in love and at peace. They would like to share these sentiments with all of you and hope you, too, feel the love for one another and the peace with all men which they have in their hearts on this day. They ask you to turn to those around you, shake hands or greet the person in some way, and say, 'Peace be with you' or 'Shalom' or 'God bless you' or whatever seems best."

I must confess I was skeptical about the outcome of this sign of peace at that wedding. The guest list included Catholics, Protestants, Jews, nonbelievers and there had been no announcement or explanation of the gesture other than the brief remarks above. But, to quote a priest observing from the side, one could actually sense the electrifying, heartwarming effect of this experience.

Later, at the reception, an usher, a young Jewish lad, went out of his way to note how overcome and at home he felt when the word "Shalom" was mentioned. During the exchange of peace two bridesmaids had to brush tears away and one husband in his early 60's tenderly kissed his wife. Someone remarked: "It made you feel kind of good all over to see everyone so close to one another."

Jeri and Dick entitled their booklet *JOY,* with the O made up of little children dancing in a circle. Along the Y they had printed, "Go in Peace. Live in Love." In an age of war and bitterness, in a period when marriage is "less wanted," perhaps more than we realize people are thirsting for peace and love, looking for courageous persons who will promise to care for each other until death do them part. Richard and Jerilyn Dali's wedding ceremony gave guests 45 minutes of exposure to just those things, then sent them home in peace, with renewed encouragement to live on in love.

Love Is Wonderful the Second Time Around

[The people mentioned here are real. However, at the doctor's request and for reasons which will become evident, their names have been changed.]

Mark Adams is a bright, competent and sensitive physician practicing internal medicine on the East Coast. His warm, personal interest in patients matches the professional skill he possesses.

Several years ago deep sorrow entered the young doctor's life. His wife, Kathleen, a quite pretty and personable woman of 28, died under tragic circumstances leaving Mark alone and with responsibility for three young children.

It was a difficult time. Many came to share his tears, offer prayers or lend support. But, as in all crises of life, ultimately the burdened individual must stand on his own, reach deep down for strength and hope, courage and faith.

In the last analysis he must either face the challenge or crawl within a shell, move on or yield to self-pity. Dr. Adams' response to this tragedy can be gleaned from these portions of his letter to a friend some months after the funeral.

"Out of this tragedy have come many blessings. . . . My friends have shown overwhelming kindness and charity; it is indescribable. I continue to be busy in practice and have mustered up unbelievable faith and courage and determination to go forward. God bless all of these folks.

"Mind you, I deeply miss my lovely Kathleen. . . . But I am at peace in this regard and know that because of her goodness and love of God and her family, she is in eternal happines with her creator. This brings me great comfort and I can claim her as my 'private litle saint.' I pray to her, ask her intercession to grant me the graces I need to carry on.

"My hope for the future is to keep the family unit together and, if I'm lucky, I can once again love another woman and be happy as I was with Kathleen. I'm sure she would want this anyway, because she loved me so much. Pray for me that I find this love."

Three years later this someone appeared, a generous, attractive girl named Jennifer who grew to love him and his family, who came to be loved in return by the widowed doctor and his motherless children.

They were married in January with a ceremony which expressed the real joy of such an event.

Upon entering the church, guests received a specially prepared, stapled booklet (cost to the groom, $30) containing words to the songs, responses for the congregation and an outline of the service.

Two nuns from the parish played guitars and led the singing of "All the Earth Proclaim the Lord," "Take Our Bread," and "They'll Know We Are Christians by Our Love."

Jennifer read the first biblical excerpt (Colossians 3:12-17, "Above all have love, which is the bond of perfection") and Mark the second. A gospel selection (John 15:9-12, "This is my commandment: love one another as I have loved you") carried on the theme of love which pervades every nuptial ceremony and permeated theirs.

After the exchange of vows at offertory time Doctor Adams' children, now older and bigger, carried gifts to the altar, presented these to their father and new mother who passed them on to the celebrant.

Before Communion, bride and groom shared love for each other by a kiss of peace, then went through the congregation conveying similar wishes to relatives and friends in the pews.

This was a beautiful wedding and an extremely happy occasion. Happy for Jennifer, radiant as any bride could be. Happy for Mark, who has discovered that his new love, while different, is, if possible, even deeper and more fulfilling than that wonderful one he knew with his first wife. Happy also, I would think, for Kathleen, his "private little saint." People who love rejoice in the happiness of a beloved. And, as Dr. Adams said, "I'm sure she would want this anyway, because she loved me so much."

Mixed Marriages

I don't remember my own parents' wedding ceremony, but I presume it took place in St. Gabriel's Catholic rectory at Hammondsport, New York. My father, you see, was an Episcopalian and my mother a devout Roman Catholic. I do recall, however, at the age of 12, some years after dad died of cancer, my mother's second marriage service. The vows were exchanged in that same rectory because my new father was also a faithful member of the Episcopal Church.

When my brother took unto himself a lovely bride, the rules had changed—slightly. The scene shifted from the parish house in that little village at the end of Lake Keuka to the church itself. We stood inside the building, but outside the sanctuary. My sister-in-law was then a Protestant (she has since become a Roman Catholic) and the Church thus manifested its discouragement of mixed marriages through this exclusion of participants from the area near God's altar.

I discovered, at the beginning of my pastoral ministry after ordination in 1956, a further easing of these restrictions with regard to the liturgical celebration of mixed marriages. Now bride and groom were permitted to come within the sanctuary and, a few years later, even to exchange nuptial promises in the context of a Mass.

Recent decrees go even further. They allow—and

ecumenists encourage—ministers from other communions to share in the Catholic ceremony by proclaiming a scriptural text or bestowing a benediction or delivering an exhortation. The latest of these decrees, an apostolic letter of March 31, 1970, *Determining Norms for Mixed Marriages,* makes it easier for couples to obtain in special situations permission to marry before a minister instead of the priest and in a church other than a Roman Catholic one. The American bishops have, as we will see in a later section, officially adapted this document to our circumstances in the United States.

These limitations, despite their radical liberalization in such a short period of time, probably seem harsh, even cruel to some. I am sure at least several readers feel a certain bitterness as they recall the uneasiness at the moment of their own mixed marriage years ago, the apparent relegation to second-class Catholic citizenship, the arguments and disapproval from clergy, family, friends. Perhaps one individual who glances at these words remembers only too well the end of a beautiful romance, the finish of a courtship—all because he wouldn't be married by the priest or she insisted on having a wedding in the Protestant church of her childhood.

The Church bears a delicate, thankless burden here. Aware that mixed marriages mean division on something vital, possible danger to an individual's faith, and complications with regard to the children, she cannot lend enthusiastic approval to them. But other Christian churches don't either and, likewise, Jews today usually take a dim view of matrimony with non-Jews. Even marital experts, from purely human considerations, wonder about the wisdom of two persons marrying who do not share similar religious beliefs. The Catholic Church, it seems, doesn't stand alone on the matter.

At the same time for many, many reasons in our pluralistic, rapidly communicating world, an ever-increasing number of men and women fall in love, face the obstacles which confront them in a mixed marriage, and decide they deeply wish to spend the rest of their lives together despite the differences and difficulties which do exist. The Church recognizes this obvious fact and urges bishops and parish priests "to aid the married couple to foster the unity of their conjugal and family life" and to "establish relationships of sincere openness and enlightened confidence with ministers of other religious communities."

The wedding liturgy can do much to cement that union, dissolve fears, and start the marriage off happily in a positive direction. Changes in Church regulations mean, in practice, that questions of who will officiate, where the service will be held, and according to what ritual are almost always resolvable. In addition, the revised Catholic rite offers a wealth of opportunities for joint planning of the ceremony—by bride, groom, priest, minister, families. Twenty-eight biblical readings plus many scripturally oriented prayers and blessings provide ready texts which should be most acceptable to all concerned. Finally, participation of clergymen from other denominations in the Roman Catholic wedding and involvement of the congregation in the ceremony itself cannot but foster good will at a time when this is most needed.

A couple begins married life when they leave the altar. Future happiness depends upon a willingness to love, understand, accept, and adjust. This perhaps is more true in a mixed marriage than in one which finds husband and wife united in their religious beliefs and attitudes. A beautiful and satisfying nuptial celebration doesn't guarantee bliss in the days ahead, but it can successfully launch bride and groom along the right course.

Help for the American Family

Apparently some have tried pre- and extramarital sex and found it wanting. That sounds like an "I told you so" observation from a conservative celibate. That conclusion, however, appeared in mustached and long-haired Phil Tracy's columns for the *National Catholic Reporter.* He feels our contemporary rush for unfettered sex before and multiple liaisons after marriage has not quite produced the liberating effects predicted by early advocates. Love, fidelity, and commitment have, Tracy believes, suffered in the process and their decline is causing, in his view, cultural chaos and much personal misery.

On the other hand, many have tried matrimony and found it difficult, too difficult to endure. *Time's* 1970 Christmas cover story, "The U.S. Family: 'Help!' " begins with a lead headline, "The American Family: Future Uncertain." Anthropologist Margaret Mead, quoted in the article, asserts: "Students in rebellion, the young people living in communes, unmarried couples living together call into question the very meaning and structure of the stable family unit as our society has known it." The magazine cites substantial "data of doom" to support a warning that our nation's families are in deep, deep trouble.

There is, I think, an encouraging sign in this otherwise bleak picture. Most couples in love and about to marry today take the step more seriously perhaps than did those who exchanged vows a decade earlier. The harsh facts of divorce and nuptial unhappiness scare them. They think long about this decision, look rather realistically at married life itself, and work hard to prepare for a future together.

Priests have recently seen that praiseworthy concern surface in couples' willingness, even eagerness to plan their own wedding ceremony. The instant and huge success of *Together for Life,* both as a booklet and filmstrip designed to help the engaged in this planning, can be explained in no other way.

The degree of such preparation for a nuptial liturgy naturally varies greatly from couple to couple. In the 50 or more weddings at which I have officiated since the new rite's introduction on Palm Sunday, 1970, every bride and groom selected the scriptural texts they preferred; most picked the prayers and blessings they wanted; about half used the Prayers of the Couple and of the Congregation provided in *Together for Life;* a few wrote their own; several produced participation booklets for the congregation.

This last item, a personally assembled "Order of Service," requires considerable time and effort from the couple, plus interest and guidance from the clergyman. Of those used at our church, one was a single mimeographed page, folded, with art work on the cover, the second, a small, stapled, xeroxed booklet, and the third, two large, carefully typed sheets, reproduced, then creased to form an 8¼" x 11" folder.

These included a greeting from bride and groom to the guests, names of those in the wedding party (including clergy, organist, servers, lectors), date and place of the ceremony, the rite's basic structure, the texts chosen, and a Prayer of the Couple. One also printed words for several hymns sung during the service and the people's responses at Mass.

The priest's advice is particularly essential if the couple decides to prepare one of these booklets. My experience indicates most people still are not familiar enough with these matters to know what should be incorporated into the text and what omitted from it. Once a few have been produced, his task becomes easier since he can supply bride and groom with models to follow.

One suggestion to spouses who opt for a commercially prepared or personally composed Prayer of the Couple: Be certain to publish this in the booklet. You probably will recite the prayer so softly that no guests can catch its phrases and then, in haste, will leave your original copy behind at the altar. This prayer normally speaks of love, fidelity and commitment. All present should hear those words; later, as husband and wife, you ought to recall them.

One Love, Different Beliefs

On Sunday afternoon or evening I regularly read the bridal section of our local paper. It brings me up to date on the status of former students or parishioners who have either recently become engaged or were married the week before. One late summer issue contained these three interesting items:

—"St. Sophia's Greek Orthodox Church was the setting last Sunday for the marriage of Miss Joyce Togias and Michael Anthony Falcone. The Rev. Michael Harmand officiated, and the Rev. Francis Horrigan gave a nuptial blessing." What is so unique about this notice? Father Horrigan serves as pastor of St. James, a Roman Catholic church in the area.

—"Miss Carolyn M. Delluomo and Peter J. Waful exchanged marriage vows in the Reformed Church of Syracuse before the Rev. Douglas Hudgston of Westminster Presbyterian Church and the Rev. William Armani of St. Theresa's Roman Catholic Church."

—"Mr. and Mrs. John Louis Andolina are residing in Portola Valley, California, following their recent wedding in Diamond Hill United Methodist Church, Berkeley Heights, N.J. Officiating at the ceremony were the Rev. Morrell Rubey and the Rev. N.N. Ashe of Little Flower Roman Catholic Church."

These arrangements were almost unheard of a decade ago. A Catholic was married in the church and by the priest, or else. But changing times require a shift in regulations and what seemed wise for previous generations often appears harmful for contemporary individuals. Obviously, Pope Paul VI, in issuing a new Apostolic Letter on Mixed Marriages, and the American bishops, in approving a statement which implements that Vatican directive, felt a more flexible policy on this matter would be beneficial.

The Falcones and the Wafuls and the Andolinas share a common trait: The partners of each marriage are one in mutual love, but different in religious beliefs. Each couple decided, no doubt after much discussion and considerable tension, the best solution to their particular situation was a wedding ceremony in the Protestant or Orthodox church with joint participation by the host clergyman and the Catholic priest.

Fortunately for them and for many others like them, Roman Catholic bishops in every diocese of the United States may now permit nuptial services of this nature. The Implementation Statement explains that development in technical terms: "When there are serious difficulties in observing the Catholic canonical form in a mixed marriage, the local Ordinary of the Catholic party or of the place where the marriage is to occur may dispense the Catholic from the observance of the form for a just pastoral cause."

The decree gives no exhaustive list of those "just pastoral causes," but does offer a few as examples. "To achieve family harmony or to avoid family alienation, to obtain parental agreement to the marriage, to recognize the significant claims of relationship or special friendship with a non-Catholic minister, to permit the marriage in a church that has particular importance to the non-Catholic."

Of course, there are other alternatives open for couples contemplating a "mixed marriage." The revised wedding rite for Roman Catholics contains many rich scriptural passages plus biblically oriented prayers and encourages bride and groom to select those most suitable for their own circumstances.

Moreover, official ecumenical principles from the Holy See and the national level suggest active involvement of the non-Catholic clergyman in Catholic wedding liturgies, especially when they are celebrated outside of Mass. Thus, religiously mixed couples may still opt for a Roman Catholic service, not out of obligation, but in preference and through free choice.

. . .

Introduction

Importance and Dignity of the Sacrament of Matrimony

1. Married Christians, in virtue of the sacrament of matrimony, signify and share in the mystery of that unity and fruitful love which exists between Christ and his Church; they help each other to attain to holiness in their married life and in the rearing and education of their children; and they have their own special gift among the people of God.

2. Marriage arises in the covenant of marriage, or irrevocable consent, which each partner freely bestows on and accepts from the other. This intimate union and the good of the children impose total fidelity on each of them and argue for an unbreakable oneness between them. Christ the Lord raised this union to the dignity of a sacrament so that it might more clearly recall and more easily reflect his own unbreakable union with his Church.

3. Christian couples, therefore, nourish and develop their marriage by undivided affection, which wells up from the fountain of divine love, while, in a merging of human and divine love, they remain faithful in body and in mind, in good times as in bad.

4. By their very nature, the institution of matrimony and wedded love are ordained for the procreation and education of children and find in them their ultimate crown. Therefore, married Christians, while not considering the other purposes of marriage of less account, should be steadfast and ready to cooperate with the love of the Creator and Savior, who through them will constantly enrich and enlarge his own family.

5. A priest should bear in mind these principles of faith, both in his instructions to those about to be married and when giving the homily during the marriage ceremony. He should relate his instructions to the texts of the sacred readings.

The bridal couple should be given a review of the fundamentals of Christian doctrine. This may include instruction on the teachings about marriage and the family, on the rites used in the celebration of the sacrament itself, and on the prayers and readings. In this way the bridegroom and the bride will receive far greater benefit from the celebration.

6. In the celebration of marriage (which normally should be within the Mass), certain elements should be stressed, especially the liturgy of the word, which shows the importance of Christian marriage in the history of salvation and the duties and responsibility of the couple in caring for the holiness of their children. Also of supreme importance are the consent of the contracting parties, which the priest asks and receives; the special nuptial blessing for the bride and for the marriage covenant; and finally, the reception of holy communion by the groom and the bride, and by all present, by which their love is nourished and all are lifted up into communion with our Lord and with one another.

7. Priests should first of all strengthen and nourish the faith of those about to be married, for the sacrament of matrimony presupposes and demands faith.

. . .

DISCUSSION QUESTIONS

1. Why do you think marriage as an institution is coming on such difficult times? Do you think newlyweds today will have to work harder for success in marital life than their parents did?
2. Do you believe a person can really fall in love more than once? Explain.
3. What, in your estimation, would be preferable: the marriage of a devout Catholic and a lukewarm, hardly practicing one or the union of a devout Catholic and devout Protestant?
4. In a mixed marriage should the couple have a nuptial Mass or a wedding liturgy outside of Mass?
5. Are contemporary love songs like "More" or "Close to You" appropriate in church for a Catholic wedding?
6. Is there any objection to holding the marriage service outside of church, e.g., on the lawn of someone's home?

part 6 / healing and help for the sick

The Sacrament of Healing

Someone said: "If you really want to hurt a person, ignore him." To be isolated, to feel alone, abandoned, set apart—that is probably man's deepest suffering.

Patients in mental hospitals should know. They often are the least visited and the ones most misunderstood. Ask yourself: How frequently do you call on that relative or friend confined in a state hospital or a private institution? How comfortable are you with him or her? Do you breathe a sigh of relief when the duty is over and you return home, free until your probing conscience pushes you back for another uneasy period with a troubled individual?

Two Servite priests, Fathers Tom LoCascio and Hugh Calkins, care for over 1,000 disturbed Catholic patients at the Elgin State Hospital in Illinois. They recently read about a Communal Rite for Anointing the Sick which had taken place on an experimental basis in Lourdes, thought it might help with this loneliness or abandonment problem in their own hospital, and asked Bishop Arthur O'Neill of the Rockford Diocese to seek permission from Rome for this revised ceremony.

The Holy See quickly said "yes" and a week before Christmas Bishop O'Neill, assisted by several dozen neighboring clergy, celebrated this Mass for the sick. Together they anointed 500 assembled in the chapel and another 500 in wards, day rooms or sickbeds.

It was a community, ecumenical venture from the very beginning. Doctors, psychiatrists, nurses, and aides helped bring patients to the Assembly Hall. A supervisory nurse read the first scriptural text (Isaiah) and the institution's superintendent a second (James 5: "The prayer of faith will save the sick man"). After the Gospel (Matthew 25: "Insofar as you did this to one of the least of these brothers of mine, you did it to me"), Bishop O'Neill preached and then began the anointing. The priests joined him, fanning out around the hall and through the buildings.

This anointment, on the forehead and outstretched hands only, stresses healing—restoration to full spiritual and physical health. A prayer after the homily and before actual administration of holy oil sums up what we hope the sacrament will accomplish.

"Redeemer of the world, we implore you by the grace of the Holy Spirit to heal these sick people of their infirmities. Forgive their sins, remove all cause of suffering, both in soul and body. By your mercy give them in abundance spiritual and bodily health. In your goodness heal them. Give them strength necessary to resume their normal activities. . . ."

Participation booklets, prepared especially for the occasion, enabled the congregation to make responses and assist with the singing. An organist played background music during the interval while the clergy were anointing patients.

Reactions? Bishop O'Neill commented: "I think we made history in the United States here today and started a trend, a trend that will and should be spreading widely to other hospitals and nursing homes, to nights for the sick in parishes, to ordinary pastoral calls on those who are ill."

The rabbi present, the ministers in attendance, and observing doctors thought it was "beautiful," "deeply impressive."

Priests from surrounding parishes liked the ceremony and saw parallel possibilities for the future.

The patients seemed awed and grateful, thrilled because the Church had come to see them, to console them, to care deeply about all they had endured and were going through. It made them feel less alone, less forgotten. The new rite did heal; it did help.

Health and Help for the Sick

The patient was in her 60's, a lovely but frightened lady gasping for breath with eyes which clearly spoke of the terrible fear she felt. Tubes carried life-sustaining oxygen into her sickly lungs while a tearful husband held his wife's hand and tried to help in some way this anxious woman, a beloved companion for over 30 years.

Before Vatican II we rushed to give such persons the "last rites"; in recent years we employed the same basic ritual but termed this sacrament instead the "anointing of the sick"; soon we will use the revised "Rites for the Sick" issued by the Holy See. There are a number of new developments in this reformed text.

1. A clearer statement of the sacrament's purpose. Its "proper grace . . . gives strength to the sick person. This grace endows him with God-given peace of soul to bear his suffering. It also effects the forgiveness of his sins, if this is necessary. And, if God so wills, the sacramental anointing can even effect a total restoration of physical health."

2. A change in the anointing procedure. "The celebration of this sacrament consists especially in the laying on of hands by the presbyters of the Church, their offering the prayer of faith and the anointing of the sick with oil sanctified by God's blessing.

"The sacrament is normally conferred by anointing the sick person on the forehead and on the hands. The words are divided so that the first part is said while the forehead is anointed, the latter part while the hands are anointed."

3. A different "form" or formula for the actual anointing. "Through this holy anointing and his great love and kindness, may the Lord fill you with the power of his Holy Spirit. In his goodness may he ease your suffering and extend his saving grace to you, freed from all the power of sin."

4. A beautiful section on the mystery of human sickness. It emphasizes we "should struggle against all sickness and carefully seek the blessings of good health, so that we can fulfill our role in human society." At the same moment it recognizes that for the sick Christian, disease and illness and death which can't be avoided have "meaning and value for their own salvation and for the world's."

5. A word of praise and encouragement for "doctors and all who are dedicated to helping the sick." "They fulfill the command of Christ to visit the sick." Our Lord implied by those words that we "should be concerned for the whole man and offer both physical relief and spiritual comfort."

6. A recognition of Viaticum as the "last rites" of the Church for a dying individual. "When the Christian, in his passage from this life, is strengthened by the body and blood of Christ, he has in it the pledge of resurrection which the Lord promised: 'He who feeds on my flesh and drinks my blood has life eternal, and I will raise him up on the last day.' "

7. A wide and flexible variety of texts. In addition to many scriptural selections, the restored ritual includes optional prayers and blessings designed for the special circumstances of sick recipients. For example, it offers formulas "when the illness is a result

of advanced age, when the sick person is in great danger, for those about to die."

8. A recommendation that we make greater use of the bible in caring spiritually for the sick. Prayers of and for the infirm "should draw primarily upon the scriptures, by meditating on those parts which speak of the mystery of human suffering in Christ and in his works or by using prayers drawn from the psalms and other parts of the bible."

I would like to recommend a little booklet, *Fear Not, I am With You,* compiled by the National Association of Catholic Chaplains and published by Alba House on Staten Island. It contains nearly 100 biblical passages relating to sickness and death with a thematic index plus many prayers for the sick and dying. A handy item to have for the hospital and home.

9. A reminder of faith's importance in this anointing rite. "The sick man will be saved by a faith that looks back to the sacrifice of the cross (which is the source of the sacrament's power) and looks ahead to the Kingdom to come (which is pledged in the sacraments)."

My fearful friend in the hospital was comforted by the anointing I administered and the prayers recited by her side that Saturday afternoon. But I think she and her worried husband would have been strengthened even more if I had followed the new ceremony.

Laymen Carrying the Eucharist to the Sick

About ten years ago this writer offered a few futuristic predictions about the liturgy of tomorrow. These not terribly original projections of things to come in the world of worship were largely based on the writings of Diekmann, Reinhold, Ellard and other giants in the liturgical movement. One suggested we might see the day in which a parent would bring to an ailing child the eucharistic sacrament and an older son or daughter would carry the consecrated host from the parish church to the sickly mother or father confined at home. Some at that time termed this particular conjecture wild, unrealistic, dreamy. However, recent developments on both sides of the Atlantic seem to indicate we may witness the introduction (or restoration) of such a practice in the near future.

This should not surprise us. Christians during the first four centuries, as a matter of standard practice, returned to their dwellings from Sunday Mass with sufficient eucharistic particles to communicate the sick and themselves throughout the week. Only later, because of many complex reasons, did the Church modify that custom and generally reserve distribution of the Blessed Sacrament to the clergy. In any event, we obviously are discussing here man-made rules and changeable legislation, not God-given doctrines and immutable commandments.

There is good justification, theologically, for the early tradition of laymen bearing the Lord to others. St. Peter writes in his first epistle: "But you are a chosen race, a royal priesthood, a consecrated nation, a people set apart to sing the praises of God . . ." (1 Pt 2:9). In the *Dogmatic Constitution on the Church,* the Council Fathers, working from this biblical text, specify in article 10 what St. Peter meant. "The baptized, by regeneration and the anointing of the Holy Spirit, are consecrated into a spiritual house and a holy priesthood."

Later in that same section, they clearly distinguish between the common priesthood of the faithful and the ministerial or hierarchical priesthood, but insist that each is a participation in the one priesthood of Christ. The priest alone "brings about the Eucharistic Sacrifice"; nevertheless, the faithful join in the offering of the Eucharist and further exercise their priesthood "by receiving the sacraments, by prayer and thanksgiving, by the witness of a holy life, and by self-denial and active charity." What better exercise of that common priesthood or what more active charity than bringing the Bread of Life to those burdened with sickness?

Hardly a week passes without notice in the press of another diocese which has deputed laymen to assist priests in the distribution of Communion at Mass. The hierarchies of Belgium and Canada (and others, presumably), however, have with permission from the Holy See extended this practice to cover other circumstances, notably cases of spiritual care for those restricted to their homes because of illness. In such instances the lay minister of Communion is delegated by the priest for a special occasion (*ad actum*) on a temporary basis. He receives the Lord himself at a parish eucharistic service and then proceeds on his mission to the sick.

The official Canadian document lists several advantages to be gained by employing these auxiliary ministers who distribute Communion to the infirm. First and of greatest significance, the sick could receive Communion more frequently, especially on Sundays and feast days. Next, there would be a closer connection between Communion for those who are ill and the parish eucharistic celebration. Third, the lay minister has more time to conduct a prolonged ceremony than the priest who must visit many persons on the same day. Finally, this practice will free the cleric to concentrate on tasks which are strictly and more properly his own.

The Belgian hierarchy, in initiating the innovation, composed an "Episcopal Letter to the Sick" to be signed by a local bishop, then presented by priests to the infirm as they visit them and inform parishioners about the new procedure. These two paragraphs excerpted from that letter nicely summarize the "why" and "how" behind this reestablishment of a very ancient tradition in the Church.

"It is very clear that only the priest can *consecrate* the bread into the Body of Christ; but from now on, your fellow Christians will be associated with him in *carrying the Eucharist*. Until now, many parishioners confined to their homes could not benefit from the Eucharist except on very infrequent occasions. They were nearly always deprived of Holy Communion on Sundays and feast days. In the future, it will be possible for you to receive Communion more frequently—particularly on Sundays.

"When you cannot go to a banquet, one of your friends often brings you a report of what took place, and tells you how much you were missed; often you are brought a piece of the cake, or a little portion of the banquet food; by these signs the community 'reaches out' to make you one of them. In your parish something similar will take place. After Mass, someone will read a part of the Sunday scriptures to you, bring you the message of the homily and 'your share' of the Lord's saving banquet, the Holy Eucharist."

From the *Constitution on the Sacred Liturgy* of Vatican II

61. Thus, for well-disposed members of the faithful, the liturgy of the sacraments and sacramentals signifies almost every event in their lives; they are given access to the stream of divine grace which flows from the paschal mystery of the passion, death, the resurrection of Christ, the font from which all sacraments and sacramentals draw their power. There is hardly any proper use of material things which cannot thus be directed toward the sanctification of men and the praise of God.

73. "Extreme Unction," which may also and more fittingly be called "anointing of the sick," is not a sacrament for those only who are at the point of death. Hence, as soon as any one of the faithful begins to be in danger of death from sickness or old age, the fitting time for him to receive this sacrament has certainly already arrived.

. . .

From the Epistle of James 5:13-16

If anyone among you is suffering hardship, he must pray. If a person is in good spirits, he should sing a hymn of praise. Is there anyone sick among you? He should ask for the presbyters of the church. They in turn are to pray over him, anointing him with oil in the Name of the Lord. This prayer uttered in faith will reclaim the one who is ill, and the Lord will restore him to health. If he has committed any sins, forgiveness will be his. Hence, declare your sins to one another, and pray for one another, that you may find healing.

From the Rite of Anointing the Sick

INTRODUCTION

I. The Mystery of Human Sickness

1. Sickness and pain have always been a heavy burden for man and an enigma to his understanding. Christians suffer sickness and pain like all other men; yet their faith helps them to understand better the mystery of suffering and to bear their pain more bravely. They know from Christ's words that their sickness has meaning and value for their own salvation and for the world's; they also know that Christ loved the sick, and that during his life he often looked upon the sick and healed them.

2. Our Redeemer taught that sickness, while it is closely related to man's sinfulness, cannot be considered a punishment which a man suffers for his personal sins. Christ himself was sinless, yet he fulfilled what is written in the book of Isaiah: he bore all the sufferings of his passion and understood human sorrow. Christ still suffers and is tormented in his followers whenever we suffer. If we realize that our sufferings are preparing us for eternal life in glory, then they will seem short and even easy to bear (see 2 Corinthians 4:17).

3. It is part of the plan laid down by God's providence that we should struggle against all sickness and carefully seek the blessings of good health, so that we can fulfill our role in human society. Yet we should always be prepared to fill up what is lacking in Christ's sufferings for the salvation of the world.

4. It is not only the sick person who should fight

against illness; doctors and all who are dedicated to helping the sick, should consider it their duty to do whatever they judge will help the sick, both physically and spiritually. In doing so, they fulfill the command of Christ to visit the sick; for Christ implied that they should be concerned for the whole man and offer both physical relief and spiritual comfort.

II. Sacraments of the Sick

A. Anointing of the Sick

5. The sacrament of anointing prolongs the concern which the Lord himself showed for the bodily and spiritual welfare of the sick, and which he asked his followers to show, also. This sacrament has its beginning in Christ, and it is spoken of in the letter of James; the Church has come to celebrate it for the faithful when they are ill.

The celebration of this sacrament consists especially in the laying on of hands by the presbyters of the Church, their offering the prayer of faith and the anointing of the sick with oil sanctified by God's blessing. This rite both signifies the grace of the sacrament and confers it.

6. The proper grace of this sacrament gives strength to the sick person. This grace endows him with God-given peace of soul to bear his suffering. It also effects the forgiveness of his sins, if this is necessary. And, if God so wills, the sacramental anointing can even effect a total restoration of physical health.

7. The anointing of the sick, which includes the prayer of faith (see James 5:15), is a sacrament of faith, just as the other sacraments are. This faith is important both for the one who administers it and particularly for him who receives it. The sick man will be saved by a faith that looks back to the sacrifice of the cross (which is the source of the sacrament's power) and looks ahead to the Kingdom to come (which is pledged in the sacraments).

. . .

DISCUSSION QUESTIONS

1. How can a good God permit suffering on earth?
2. Why are Catholics often afraid to call or have a priest when someone is seriously ill? What can be done or said to reassure such people?
3. Do you think it is practically feasible to have laymen bring Communion to the sick as suggested above?

part 7 / death and resurrection

Evening Funerals: An Example

Judy Wilson was an apparently healthy and typically sweet, innocent, lovable fourth-grader at Holy Family Parish in Harrisburg, Pennsylvania. In the fall of 1969, however, a massive brain disease suddenly snuffed out this young girl's life and brought intense sorrow into the hearts of many.

The liturgical commission for the Harrisburg Diocese, under Bishop Joseph T. Daley's chairmanship, had only a few days earlier issued guidelines for the optional celebration of funeral Masses in the evening. Father James LaCroce, who at that time doubled as pastor of Holy Family and executive secretary of the diocesan liturgy committee, felt this might be an excellent occasion to introduce the new regulations. He asked Judy's grief-stricken parents if they would care to hold the funeral service in church at night instead of according to the more customary morning arrangement. The mother and father readily agreed, and must have thanked God a thousand times since for helping them make this decision.

Viewing of the body began at 6 p.m. with the family greeting visitors in the church lobby. A priest stepped into the confessional around 7:30 as a convenience for those awaiting the Mass scheduled to start a half hour later. When Father LaCroce walked to the vestibule for the entrance rite of the funeral liturgy, his small church was packed to capacity with some 450 mourners.

The understandable mourning gradually turned into Christian joy. White vestments, songs of hope and eternal life, readings about Jesus' power to raise us from the dead, prayers seeking peace for Judy and courage for her family, a personal homily connecting the good news of salvation with the human tragedy of this moment—these things slowly lifted heavy feelings and downcast hearts. All of those voices united in song and prayer, all of those people simply being there and lending the support which mere presence can give, all of those individuals sharing a common sorrow and a common faith in the resurrection created an almost overwhelming atmosphere of love and encouragement.

There were tearful, poignant moments, too. Especially at the offertory when parents brought the bread and wine, classmates carried a gift for the parish in her honor, and a friend bore Judy's World Mission Bank with its carefully saved coins for the poor of this world.

The young child's awareness of others' needs came from an expected source—her father and mother. They asked, for example, that money used for traditional flowers be sent instead to the March of Dimes foundation, a request prompted by their daughter's special interest in a crippled boy featured on one of its campaign posters. Several months after the funeral, these parents gave further indication of their Christian care for the indigent by bringing all of their little girl's clothes to the rectory with a wish that they be distributed among needy families.

The theme throughout the evening, of course, was one of victory over defeat, life over death. A hymn sung during the service spoke of "Let hymns of joy to grief succeed." That movement from aching sorrow to peaceful elation came, however, as I mentioned, rather gradually. This evening funeral was the first one for the diocese and Father LaCroce had asked a photographer to capture on film some highlights of the service. Standing unobtrusively in the back he caught with his zoom lens camera the faces of both family and friends at various moments during Mass. Later, as he developed these pictures, the artist could not believe the transformation in the immediate family's expression from pained grief at the offertory to an almost radiant happiness at the final blessing.

This funeral liturgy's power to console was due in large part to the presence of so many persons who came to tender their love and prayers both for Judy and her family. Unfortunately, our busy business world today does not permit us to leave work for a morning burial service except in special instances. In lieu of that we visit the mortician's parlor or deceased's home to pay respects, leave a Mass card, and whisper a brief prayer. These are marvelous ways of comforting the afflicted, but wouldn't full participation in a eucharistic funeral celebration be even better?

The Harrisburg liturgy commission feels the answer to that question is "yes." In the next section I will describe its guidelines for evening funerals which made possible such total involvement in Judy Wilson's resurrection liturgy.

Evening Funerals: General Principles

"The time to give witness to resurrection theology is the time of the death of a Christian. The way to give this witness is through the memorial rite, the Mass, which was given to us by Christ for the purpose of celebrating his death, resurrection and entrance into glory—as well as our own. Because of the rhythm of life and work today it is becoming increasingly more difficult for friends and parishioners to assist at a funeral Mass during the day."

These words from guidelines of the Harrisburg liturgical commission give the theological base and practical reason for its encouragement of evening funeral services.

A change like this affects many persons besides the bereaved. Undertakers, florists, priests, organists—these and others must alter long-established habits when a family chooses to celebrate the funeral at night. We should expect a natural reluctance on their part and perhaps some heated opposition to the suggestion. The Harrisburg commission, particularly through its executive secretary, Father James LaCroce, and the diocesan chancellor, Msgr. William Keeler, attempted to anticipate these objections by advance discussions, especially with area funeral directors.

These men displayed some hesitation at the outset and mentioned the increased costs in terms of transportation, lighting, personnel. However, they proved most cooperative and realized that cultural patterns affecting burial of the dead will change very slowly indeed. This has been the experience in Harrisburg and in the nearby diocese of Camden, New Jersey. Msgr. Keating of the liturgy department in the latter diocese once reported that over a fairly long interval only two parishes sought permission for funerals at night, even though priests in both churches found the innovation extremely successful. In Father LaCroce's own Holy Family Church a few, but not many, have requested an evening service since the burial of young Judith Wilson.

An item-by-item account of details in the Harrisburg directive will quickly reveal its content:

1. The evening funeral service is optional, left to the wishes of the deceased's family.

2. No evening funerals are to take place on Saturday or Sunday.

3. Burial would in most cases take place the next morning from the funeral parlor.

4. Viewing of the body may be held in the church lobby, a room or hall adjacent to the church, or in the church proper. A book for signing by visitors would be in order. Any reservations a family has concerning the viewing should be respected.

5. "Flower cards," much like gift certificates, can be purchased from the florist and given to the parish. These will be redeemed for flowers at some future date for use in the church in memory of the deceased. This resolves in a practical way the legitimate desires of friends and the understandable anxiety of florists.

6. A priest should be available for confessions a half hour before time of the funeral Mass.

7. Some type of simple reception for the congregation afterwards in a parish hall is very desirable when circumstances permit.

8. The viewing in church is limited to one night. Priests may object that evening hours are always

crowded with appointments. However, some of this time in the past has been spent in travel to funeral parlors for devotional prayers and calls of condolence. Moreover, the impact on many people of a well-attended, fully participated evening funeral rite like Judy Wilson's and the great solace such a service supplies the mourning family would seem to outweigh any inconvenience this new arrangement causes parish priests.

The introductory catechesis of these Harrisburg guidelines offers further doctrinal support for evening funeral Masses.

"In its renewal of the funeral rite the Church stresses the victorious character of Christian death through its selection of ceremonies, readings, prayers, music and color of vestments. True, we will always experience the need to lament and weep for our departed loved ones, as did Jesus. But it is surely appropriate that some time before burial the Christian *community* should *celebrate,* with some signs of joy, the belief that a brother or sister has entered the newness of eternal life. Otherwise it would be difficult to see how our affirmation of the resurrection could have any real or honest meaning.

"If our belief in resurrection has no way of being adequately expressed by the community on the occasion of death, of what 'Christian' value is our sentimental tribute to the one who has fallen asleep in Christ? If friends and parishioners are limited to viewing a dead body, accompanied with some private devotions, are we not failing in giving full witness to our faith's most cherished belief at a time when witness could be most effective?"

When a loved one dies we need two things more than anything else: faith in the resurrection and the support of friends. Evening funerals may make it easier in a busy society for friends to strengthen our faith and offer that support when we feel crushed by the death of a person near and dear to us.

The New Funeral Rite

Do you think we generally go to excess in making funeral arrangements for a departed beloved? Are we almost forced to put on a show, select a casket beyond our means, follow an artificial protocol? Or do you feel lengthy calling hours, a solemn religious service, and the body's careful interment express respect for the deceased, faith in the resurrection, and love of the bereaved?

The revised funeral rite, issued in Latin on August 15, 1969, and now in use with an English translation, doesn't really provide certain answers to these provocative questions. Article 2 of the Introduction merely states that "family traditions, local customs, groups established to take care of funerals, anything that is good may be used freely, but anything alien to the gospel should be changed. . . ."

Authorities in Rome have, with wisdom, stepped lightly in this area, leaving the judgment about specific practices to bishops and other individuals in each country. The restored ritual insists only that a funeral service celebrate Christ's paschal mystery and the dead person's share in Jesus' victory over death.

Catholics in many sectors of the United States found the new rite very similar to an experimental liturgy for Christian burial which had been employed in a majority of dioceses several years prior to the revised ritual's publication. Themes of joy, hope and triumph prevail in such a service with a variety of texts, actions and signs communicating to family and friends those sentiments.

▪ The funeral ritual (like baptismal and marriage books released earlier) possesses an element of flexibility made possible through its extensive collection of biblical readings (42), psalms (17), and prayers. Preliminary directives suggest that a priest use those texts which best fit the wishes of the deceased's family and as much as possible "involve them in planning the funeral celebration and the choice of the options made available in this rite" (art. 25).

▪ White vestments, symbolic not necessarily of the departed's innocence, but of his hoped-for rising to a glorious life, may be worn instead of black or purple.

▪ The large paschal candle, carried in procession and placed near the casket, links together an entire network of related notions—Baptism, the resurrection, Easter and, of course, entrance into eternal bliss.

▪ The rite after Mass, once called absolution, now has been changed to a service of final commendation. This is "not to be understood as a purification of the dead—which is effected rather by the eucharistic sacrifice—but as the last farewell with which the Christian community honors one of its members before the body is buried" (art. 10).

▪ "The sprinkling with holy water, which recalls the person's entrance into eternal life through Baptism, and the incensation, which honors the body of the deceased as temple of the Holy Spirit, may also be considered signs of farewell" (art. 10).

▪ A period of prayer between the time of death and burial ought to be arranged so people can pray for the dead and profess their own faith in eternal life. The introductory norms, while not mentioning or certainly prohibiting the customary rosary at "wakes," do show partiality for scriptural prayer services. Biblical readings in such circumstances "proclaim the paschal mystery, support the hope of reunion in the Kingdom of God, teach respect for the dead, and encourage the witness of Christian living" (art. 11).

▪ Burial of the body in a grave or tomb, "as the Lord himself willed to be buried," enjoys the Church's preference, but cremation is permitted as long as the reasons for selecting this process are not "contrary to Christian principles" (art. 15).

▪ The cemetery prayers more actively involve mourners who stand by the grave for those final moments before the body is lowered into its resting place. They include a prayer of the faithful in which the community present prays for the departed and for the survivors, "Lord, you wept at the death of Lazarus, your friend: comfort us in our sorrow. We ask this in faith." R. "Lord hear our prayer." "You raised the dead to life: give our brother (sister) eternal life. We ask this in faith. . . ."

▪ Songs and psalms which express grief but strengthen hope should, whenever possible, form part of the rite. "The Strife Is O'er, the Battle Won" or "To Jesus Christ Our Sovereign King" already are funeral hymns familiar to many which convey the correct concepts of triumph and resurrection.

The theological foundation for these ritual practices can be summed up in words from article 1 of the funeral rite: "Those who in baptism have become one with the dead and risen Christ will pass from death to life, to be purified in soul and welcomed into the fellowship of the saints in heaven. They look forward in blessed hope to his second coming and the bodily resurrection of the dead." These prayers and burial services "which bring spiritual help to some may bring to others a consoling hope."

Together at Death

John and Nellie Schmid would have celebrated their golden jubilee, if a car accident had not killed them both several months before the anniversary date. That long life together produced a long list of descendants—10 children, 38 grandchildren, and one great-grandchild.

All, or at least most of these progeny, gathered together on a cold Minnesota night some hours after the tragedy to hear how it happened, to decide on details of the burial, and to plan the funeral liturgy.

These saddened people listened calmly to accounts of the mishap and quickly, easily arrived at decisions concerning the estate. But when they turned to a discussion of the Mass for their parents and grandparents, the agreement ended and animated confrontation began.

One son, Giles, who then served as director of planning and evaluation for the United States Catholic Conference's Department of Education, outlined some of the optional texts, hymns, and practices available for them to use, even made a few suggestions of his own.

Not everyone concurred, to say the least. But they aired their feelings, talked things through, and at the finish never felt so close as a family.

As a first step they looked over the Jerusalem Bible for two pertinent scriptural readings. Then the

Schmids thought about appropriate hymns (familiar enough for full congregational singing) and how a maximum number of persons could be involved in the service itself.

Finally, they called a local church publishing shop and made arrangements for it to print a leaflet with the special music and responses selected for the funeral.

An attractive cover of this folder featured a crown and a plant, symbols of the living hope which Christians should possess. In addition, the frontispiece carried these words: "Be faithful unto death and I will give thee a crown of life."

Many did in fact take an active part in the funeral liturgy of John and Nell Schmid.

▪ A daughter read the first reading. "There is a season for everything, a time for every occupation under heaven: A time for giving birth, a time for dying. . . ."

▪ The parish administrator, a close priest friend, offered the Mass and proclaimed the gospel message about resurrection and life everlasting.

▪ After the celebrant's homily different members of the family made a few remarks about their parents, or their grandparents and how this couple's Christian example had affected them.

▪ Grandchildren brought gifts to the altar in procession at the proper moment.

▪ A friend of Mr. Schmid who for years had sung with him in the choir did a solo version of *Panis Angelicus* at Communion time which was followed by the community's singing of "The Lord is my shepherd, nothing shall I want."

▪ The entire congregation filled the church at the conclusion with "Glory, glory, hallelujah . . . Mine eyes have seen the glory of the coming of the Lord."

The revised funeral rite notes, in its introductory principles, various duties of the priest at the time of a parishioner's death. He should "show loving concern for the family of the deceased person, support them in the time of sorrow, and as much as possible involve them in planning the funeral celebration and the choice of the options made available in the rite."

The Schmid funeral illustrated in concrete terms these abstract directives. That family, together so frequently before, drew together again at the death of the two who had given them life. This jointly planned liturgy expressed their deep love for the mother and dad, the grandfather and grandmother, lent one another mutual support during a painful time, offered an example to others, and gave all present hope for the future.

Celebrating Death

Millions of readers and viewers have sobbed through Erich Segal's *Love Story*. Critics may judge his novel and movie harshly but the fact remains that for many reading the book or watching the film was a very emotional experience.

Why? The tale itself—a beautiful 25-year-old wife dying of a rare disease—naturally tends to bring tears. But I think the deeper, stronger reason is that most people personalize *Love Story*. Within their hearts they wonder: How would I feel in similar circumstances? What would I say?

No one knows how he would feel or what he would say, but words like "rejoice" or "celebrate" seem far off the mark. I mean, would you tell Oliver Barrett IV to rejoice because Jennie has gone home to God or would you speak to him about the celebration of a Christian's death? Hardly.

First comes the sharing of a bereaved's sorrow, then follows the sowing of hope for a future. Introductory principles of the renewed funeral text set these two elements as the purpose of a Christian burial service.

"Between the time of death and burial there should be sufficient opportunities for the people to pray for the dead and to profess their own faith in eternal life. . . . In this way the compassionate kindness of Mother Church and the consolation of the faith may lighten the burden of believers without offending those who mourn."

In certain ways we best can comfort the survivors and share their grief during calling hours at the family residence or funeral home. Here is an occasion for mutual tears, supportive embraces, helpful words, consoling prayers. Perhaps in such a context the priest should wear for the wake service a purple stole (a blend between the severe black and joyful white) or a green one (symbolic of hope).

But we also begin the healing, hopeful process at this time. Gentle reminders that death is not simply an end but also a beginning, that it signals not only a departure but likewise an entrance, that it brings painful separation, true, but promises future reunion can suggest to the bereaved thoughts of resurrection and everlasting life.

Biblical passages help. "These readings proclaim the paschal mystery, support the hope of reunion in the Kingdom of God, teach respect for the dead, and encourage the witness of Chistian living." That section (no. 11) from the Revised Rite of Funerals indicates why the Church prefers a scripturally oriented prayer service at the wake.

This sensitivity to the anguish of mourners while still preaching Jesus' victory over death should carry over to the funeral Mass. A rousing alleluia at the start may prove too much of a clash with the still heavy hearts of the deceased's family.

Later, after the songs and symbols, the prayers and readings, the liturgical ceremonies and the celebrant's words have exerted their influence and created a different climate, Palestrina's alleluia-filled hymn probably will reflect in perfect fashion the transformed feelings of those present.

The burial of a Christian truly is or should be a celebration of death. We rejoice that he or she who was buried in Baptism with Jesus, who followed Christ in faith through life, now passes through death to perfect joy with the Lord face-to-face forever. But those left behind have an empty ache and lonely tears in the midst of their confident hope for future reunion. A funeral service must fuse within it both the sorrow and the celebration.

Until We Meet Again

Mary Finnegan lived a full 77 years, but her death early Christmas morning still came unexpectedly, literally in that middle of the night the gospel texts mention. She rose from bed at 2:00 a.m., walked to the living room of their attractive home and complained to her concerned husband about "never having felt like this before." In a matter of moments she sat down, stood up, then sat again, slumped over and was gone.

Mrs. Finnegan was a refined lady, a strong person and a good woman. She left behind, besides her spouse, two children, sons in their forties—one a most successful architect, the other a priest classmate of mine. In addition, three very special children found themselves suddenly without their paternal grandmother.

Before the funeral the father, mother and uncle of these elementary and preelementary school youngsters pondered a common problem facing survivors in situations like this. "Should we bring the boys and the little girl to the wake? to the funeral? to the cemetery? Would these be harmful or helpful experiences for them?"

They decided "yes" on all counts and as I watched the family from my sanctuary vantage point during the service, I concluded they certainly had judged wisely.

The little ones participated in the beautiful burial of a Christian. There were tears to be sure and an occasional cracking of the priest-son's voice. But the dominant atmosphere was one of serene hope, quiet resignation, and joyful anticipation. A great crowd of fellow believers—three bishops, priests by the dozens, and a church filled with friends—gathered as a community to bid Mary farewell, temporarily, and to commend her to the Lord.

Jimmy, Patrick and Maura caught, in their own limited way, all of this drama. They tasted the painful reality of death and separation, but also felt that positive joy which flows from faith in the resurrection.

These children watched their father and mother walk up into the sanctuary and read the first scriptural passages. They heard the strong voices of men (mainly) and women singing songs which in Alleluia terms spoke of victory and a fuller life after death. "Keep in mind that Jesus Christ has died for us and is risen from the dead; he is our saving Lord, he is joy for all ages."

They observed their uncle, vested in white and assisted by eight other priests, leading the congregation in prayer and concelebrating Mass. They saw a bishop offer the final prayer and a blessing over the body. They heard this older man with a red cap speak soft, personal words of comfort to their father and grandfather.

Then, of course, there were other silent signs to be noticed. The handsome white pall, for example, draped over the casket, a reminder of Mary's Baptism so many years ago and the present hope it offers for her personal triumph over death. Or the sign of peace exchanged between all the clergy in the sanctuary and carried down into the pews among the congregation. Or the sprinkling of water and burning of incense, the former recalling a baptismal ceremony in the past and the latter promising a bodily resurrection in the future. Or the burning Easter candle placed before the bier as a symbol of Jesus' and our conquest of sin and destruction.

True Christian that she was, Mary Finnegan in younger days and to the end had lent caring, sharing, helping hands to neighbors in need. The homilist for this funeral liturgy, now the Finnegan's pastor, but once a next-door friend, remembered those past kind deeds and spoke of them to the congregation. He was not the only beneficiary of her sensitive concern. Many in the church had felt that touch in former years and came to pay their respects, to send this lady on her way to God.

The rite of final commendation and farewell at the Mass's conclusion expresses this rather well. During it, a united group of believing relatives and friends assembled for the last time to say "good-bye" or, better, "until we meet again." "Father, into your hands we commend our sister, Mary. . . . Lord, hear our prayer: Welcome Mary to paradise and help us to comfort each other with the assurance of our faith until we all meet in Christ to be with you and with our sister, Mary, forever."

It seems to me that fully participated Christian burial service should have left a lasting and healthy impression on those Finnegan children. They must have sensed the full picture, the sorrow and serenity, the beauty and pain of a loved one's death. Later, instead of fearing the dark and unknown, perhaps they will be able to say with St. Paul, "O death, where is your victory? O death, where is your sting?"

From the Gospel according to John 6:47-51

"Let me firmly assure you, he who believes has eternal life. I am the bread of life. Your ancestors ate manna in the desert, but they died. This is the bread that comes down from heaven for a man to eat and never die. I myself am the living bread come down from heaven. If anyone eats this bread he shall live forever; the bread I will give is my flesh for the life of the world."

. . .

From the Rite of Funerals

The priest may then sprinkle the body with holy water saying these or similar words:

I bless the body of N., with the holy water that recalls his (her) baptism of which Saint Paul writes: All of us who were baptized into Christ Jesus were baptized into his death. By baptism into his death we were buried together with him, so that just as Christ was raised from the dead by the glory of the Father, we too might live a new life. For if we have been united with him by likeness to his death, so shall we be united with him by likeness to his resurrection.

A white pall, in remembrance of the baptismal garment, may then be placed on the coffin by the pallbearers or others, and the priest may say these or similar words:

On the day of his (her) baptism, N. put on Christ. In the day of Christ's coming, may be (she) be clothed with glory.

From the *Constitution on the Sacred Liturgy* of Vatican II

Art. 8

In the earthly liturgy we take part in a foretaste of that heavenly liturgy which is celebrated in the holy city of Jerusalem toward which we journey as pilgrims, where Christ is sitting at the right hand of God, a minister of the holies and of the true tabernacle; we sing a hymn to the Lord's glory with all the warriors of the heavenly army; venerating the memory of the saints, we hope for some part and fellowship with them; we eagerly await the Saviour, Our Lord Jesus Christ, until He, our life, shall appear and we too will appear with Him in glory.

Art. 81

The rite for the burial of the dead should express more clearly the paschal character of Christian death, and should correspond more closely to the circumstances and traditions found in various regions. This holds good also for the liturgical color to be used.

DISCUSSION QUESTIONS

1. Do you think present burial customs in the United States mirror the Christian view of death or represent an attempt to conceal the reality of a loved one's demise?
2. Discuss the meaning and effectiveness of these Catholic symbols in the funeral liturgy: the pall, sprinkling with holy water, incense, paschal candle, white vestments, resurrection music, Mass and Holy Communion.
3. Should preadolescent children be brought to a wake, funeral, cemetery?
4. Explain the question of an open or closed casket, burial in a grave or cremation in terms of today's world and the Christian message.
5. Would evening funerals be successful in your neighborhood?